Solving Sheetfed Offset Press Problems

by
GATF Staff

Graphic Arts Technical Foundation
4615 Forbes Avenue
Pittsburgh, Pennsylvania 15213-3796
Telephone: 412/621-6941
Fax: 412/621-3049

Paper compliments of:

Halopaque – 100 • 60-pound Satin
100% Deinked Fiber • 20% Post Consumer

Foreword

Solving Sheetfed Offset Press Problems is not a textbook on press operation. Instead, it is a convenient reference guide to help press operators to identify press problems and their most likely causes and to find quick solutions.

In addition to an index, the book's extensive table of contents makes it easy to locate a particular printing problem. Accompanying each problem description is a list of possible causes and proven remedies. A systematic study of this book will provide the press operator with an understanding of the factors that tend to create problems, often making it possible to avoid some problems altogether in the future.

The practical experience of a number of GATF specialists has made this book possible. Lloyd P. DeJidas, Brad E. Evans, Frank J. Gualtieri, Frederick W. Higgins, John E. Peters, Raymond J. Prince, Kenneth E. Rizzo, and Murray I. Suthons reviewed the previous edition of this book, updating the information and adding new problems, causes, and remedies wherever necessary. Robert J. Schneider, Jr., assistant editor with the Technical Information Group, incorporated their comments into this third edition of *Solving Sheetfed Offset Press Problems* and edited the manuscript.

Thomas M. Destree
Editor in Chief

Contents

8. Ink Problems

Introduction

This book is for press operators with general knowledge of sheetfed lithographic offset press operation and specific knowledge of the manufacturer's instructions for setting and adjusting units and controlling the operation of the particular press involved.

A single-color
duplicator
*Courtesy of
A.B. Dick Co.*

A six-color sheetfed
press
*Courtesy of MAN-
Roland*

A single-color
duplicator
*Courtesy of
Ryobi Limited*

Other GATF publications provide general instruction in press operations. The specialized information required to operate any press properly is contained in the operating manuals supplied with the press. If these are not available, they can be obtained from the manufacturer or the manufacturer's successor. Standard sizes for sheetfed lithographic offset presses, other than duplicators, range from 14½×20½ in. (370×520 mm) to 58×77 in. (1473×1956 mm) capacity. Offset duplicators usually print 8½×11 in. (216×280 mm) or 11×17 in. (280×432 mm). Other major variations are in number of printing units, the dampening system used, and whether the press is perfecting or nonperfecting.

Yet even a knowledgeable and experienced press operator may find, after the various units have been adjusted and the plate has been brought to running conditions, that when the

A single-color
duplicator
*Courtesy of
AM International, Inc.*

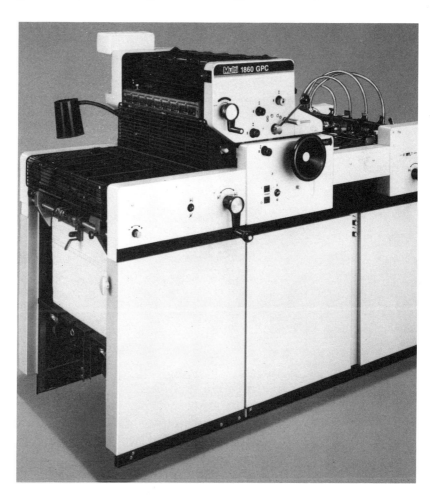

run gets under way, puzzling problems sometimes occur, immediately or later. The problem is usually seen in a defective printed sheet and the cause is not immediately evident. Correcting such problems may involve trying several different solutions, which takes a lot of time. Using this book should reduce the amount of time required to solve problems.

The sources of the problem may lie in the press, in the materials that come together in the press, or in conditions that develop during the run. Combinations of mechanical and chemical variables as well as raw materials such as paper and ink may contribute to a wide variety of problems. Controlling these variables and quickly identifying and solving existing or potential problems will reduce downtime and increase productivity and profitability.

Often, problems have many sources. If paper and ink are incompatible, changing either one may solve the problem. Paper, ink, and dampening solution may all contribute to problems. The dampening solution may be too acidic or improperly diluted. The paper may be linty, or dusty, or not flat. The ink may be too short, too cold, too tacky, or have insufficient drier. Ink rollers may be fouled with paper lint.

A four-color
sheetfed press
*Courtesy of Komori
America Corp.*

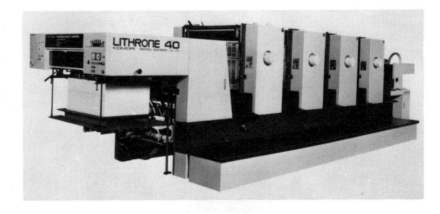

Ink may have built up, caked, or piled on roller surfaces, the plate, or blanket. Gum may have dried over a plate.

What an operator sees first is not the source of the problem (e.g., a loose blanket, worn shaft bushings) but the unsatisfactory appearance of the printed sheet. The problem may be something that disturbs the run such as paper that misfeeds or pulls out of the grippers. The most common problem during the run is the printed sheet defect. The image areas may be slurred, doubled, or printed too light. The solids may be snowflaky or contain ghost images; weak areas may extend backward from the leading edges of solids. Halftones may sharpen and lose highlight dots, or appear grainy. There may be uneven impression, color variation, or the color misregister. Hickeys, or other kinds of spots, streaks, or stains may appear. The sheets may be wrinkled, creased, or curled on delivery or after standing in delivery piles. Ink may pick, split, or tear the paper, set off in the delivery pile, or rub off in folding and binding operations.

These are the symptoms. The press operator must determine the cause of a problem so that it can be corrected or diminished quickly.

The organization and index of this book should help to locate and diagnose press problems. Because defects in the printed sheet have many causes, the specific characteristics of the defects are analyzed to pinpoint the most probable cause or causes.

Determining the cause of a problem may make the remedy evident, but often a choice must be made. If the source of the difficulty lies in the paper, changing the condition (such as the moisture content) or replacing defective paper with another lot may not be feasible, and the best solution may be reducing the problem without totally correcting it. In this book, alternative remedies are sometimes provided for particular problems.

Continued experience with this book should help prevent many problems from arising at all.

1 Sheet Feeding and Delivery Problems

Among the requirements for successful press operation is the smooth and consistent flow of paper through the press. This, in turn, depends on two primary conditions. First, the paper must be flat and free from curl, and it must be properly piled and lined up in the feeder. Second, all sheet-handling elements of the press must be properly adjusted and timed.

Feeder elements that require adjustments include suckers, hold downs, air blasts, forwarding wheels, and tapes. Next, the front guides, side guide, insertion device, and impression cylinder grippers are adjusted to register the sheets with the printing unit. On multicolor presses, two or more impression cylinders are involved, together with the necessary transfer cylinders, and all their grippers must be in proper adjustment. Finally, delivery bar grippers must carry the sheets to the delivery pile and drop them in position to be jogged.

If any one of the necessary conditions is not met, the result is a press problem that needs to be located and remedied. In some cases, correction may be simple; in others, it may be complicated, requiring the attention of a press manufacturer's service technician.

The following is a list of the more common feeder and delivery problems encountered in sheetfed press operation, together with their principal causes and known remedies.

Problem 1.   **The feeder misses or feeds double.**

Cause A: The pile is not at the proper feeding height. If it is too high, it is likely to feed more than one sheet at a time. If it is too low, it is likely to miss sheets.

A Spiess unitized feeder

Remedy:
Raise or lower the feeder pile until the top sheet is about ¼ in. (6 mm) below the top of the front sheet-control flaps; then, set the height governor and adjust the suckers.

Cause B: Too much separation air blast with nozzle set too low.

Remedy:
Readjust the air blast nozzle to the proper height, and reduce the air pressure.

Cause C: Suckers not performing properly.

Remedy 1:
If the suckers are dirty, clean them and keep them clean.

Remedy 2:
If the suckers are worn out, replace them.

Remedy 3:
On older equipment, clean the rotary valve in the feeder head assembly.

Remedy 4:
If the suckers need adjusting, set the separating suckers so that they just contact the top sheet with the pile at the proper height. This contact should be made with the face of

the sucker parallel to the surface of the sheet and with the separation air working.

Remedy 5:
Check vacuum timing. With single-sheet feeders, the front suckers should be set to contact the top sheet as it floats on the separating air. If the suckers push the top sheet down on the pile, there is the possibility of picking up two sheets or of missing the sheet completely.

With stream feeders where the forwarding suckers are at the back, the forwarding suckers should be adjusted so that the separating suckers lift the sheets to them.

More than one design of sucker is available. Follow the press manufacturer's instructions regarding where and when to use each sucker. Use maximum vacuum at all times. If paper is deformed or cracked, use restricted suckers.

Cause D: Sheets are stuck together by trimmer.

Remedy:
Air the stock. Flip through the lift to be sure sheets do not stick to each other.

Cause E: Static in paper.

Remedy 1:
Insert ionizing air cartridges in the air blast lines. These cartridges should be changed yearly.

Remedy 2:
Maintain RH of air in the pressroom above 35%. (Note: Paper performs best at 50±5% RH, but static is largely eliminated above 35% RH.)

Problem 2.   **The feeder forwards sheets unevenly.**

Cause A: Too much or too little air blast under the separated top sheet. Too much air ripples sheets excessively and produces waves between forwarding wheels, causing uneven forwarding.

Remedy:
Use just enough air blast to float the top sheet. If the sheets

have a tendency to stick, it is better to repile the load, rolling the lifts to free the sheets, rather than try to separate them with excess air.

Cause B: Rotary valve not clean. Grooves cut into the rotary valve get clogged with spray powder, oil, and debris. This valve controls the vacuum and air blast at the suckers. If one forwarding sucker turns on before the other, the sheet could be twisted as it is fed down the feedboard. This makes the feeder forward the sheet unevenly.

Remedy:
Keep the rotary valve clean.

Cause C: Incorrect alignment of air blast nozzles.

Remedy:
Align nozzles properly.

Problem 3.   **Oil from the vacuum/air pump stains sheets on the feeder.**

Cause: An overheated or improperly oiled compressor. Its overheating can be due to neglect, using the wrong oil, or running at too high a pressure. When overheated, the oil vaporizes and then condenses while going through the blower pipes. One of the most common errors in oiling a compressor is overoiling.

Remedy:
Follow the press instruction manual on oiling and maintaining pumps. Adjust the relief valve to keep the air pressure at the proper level. Flush the pump at least twice a year, following instructions on the pump for the correct solvent and flushing procedure.

Problem 4.   **Sheets cock or jam on the conveyor.**

Cause A: On a single-sheet (sheet-by-sheet) feeder, the two forwarding wheels are not dropping at exactly the same time.

Remedy:
Adjust the timing of the wheels.

Cause B: Forwarding wheels dented, not aligned, or glazed.

Remedy:
Put new rubber on the wheels. Set wheels on the forwarding roller according to the manufacturer's specification for setting up the feed board.

Cause C: Tapes that have frayed or developed small breaks, or tapes with loose stitching. Such defects can damage the back edges of the sheets or crumple and jam sheets that are stopped by the front guides.

Remedy:
Put on new tapes.

Cause D: Rust or moisture on the feed table.

Remedy:
Keep the feed table clean.

Cause E: Curling of the front edges or corners of sheets that fail to enter the side guide, causing sheets to cock and jam.

Remedy:
Repile the sheets, rolling down or decurling the front edge and corners.

Cause F: Buildup of static in the stock or from movement of the feed tapes.

Remedy 1:
Install commercial static elimination equipment.

Remedy 2:
Humidify the pressroom if the RH is low.

Problem 5: **Front register varies from sheet to sheet.**

Cause A: Not enough clearance under the hold-down springs or fingers.

Remedy:
When running thin papers, adjust the clearance with a feeler gauge to just clear the thickness of the paper being run. For papers over 0.010 in. (0.25 mm) thick, adjust the clearance to 1½ times the paper thickness.

Cause B: Too much clearance under the hold-down springs or fingers. This condition allows the sheets to buckle or bounce back from the stops.

Remedy:
Adjust the clearance as described for Cause A.

Cause C: Tail-end wheels are too far back or too far forward.

Remedy:
Reset tail-end wheels for proper position just off the tail end of the sheets and directly behind the registering front stop. Use steel or soft brush wheels only (no rubber wheels) on the back edge of the paper.

Cause D: Gripper edge or tail end of sheets not perfectly straight, or sheets vary in length from front to back. The results are the same as if the tail-end wheels were not properly set.

Remedy:
Replace or retrim the stock.

Cause E: Not enough tension in the impression cylinder grippers. Tack of the ink causes sheets to slip in the grippers with resulting misregister.

Remedy 1:
Clean the grippers, and reset them regularly. Folding carton presses normally need to have the grippers reset and cleaned every three months.

Remedy 2:
Replace gripper pads if they are worn.

Remedy 3:
Check the grippers for uniform tension. Increase the tension if necessary.

Cause F: Convex or concave gripper edge of paper. This condition does not cause a problem in a three-point register system. Multiple front guides can cause parts of the gripper edge to buckle or the sheets to be gripped at different angles, creating bad fit, front-edge misregister, wrinkles, and other problems.

Remedy:
Check the straightness of the gripper edge trim of the paper. If it is not straight, retrim or replace the paper. Adjusting stops to fit improperly trimmed paper may get the stock through the press, producing printed sheets that cannot be fed through a folder or binding machine.

Cause G: Grippers on swing or rotary feed mechanism are not synchronized with impression cylinder grippers. This condition may be due to wear of the device that positions the gripper bar of the inserter in relation to the cylinder grippers at the instant of transfer.

Swing-feed insertion system *(left)*

Feed-roll insertion system *(right)*

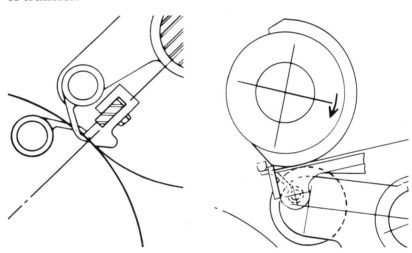

Remedy:
Replace worn parts.

Cause H: Improper timing of the overfeed roll mechanism.

Remedy 1:
Adjust timing of the overfeed roll so that the sheets buckle slightly as they are pushed into the gripper openings and against the cylinder stops.

Remedy 2:
Adjust front stops. Graduated front stops, available on some presses, will compensate for unevenly cut paper.

Problem 6.   **Side guiding varies from sheet to sheet (push side guide).**

Cause A: Paper is trimmed unevenly or out of square.

                                Remedy:
                                Retrim the paper, or use properly cut stock.

Cause B: Pusher plate is not parallel to the edge of the sheet. This condition can cause variable buckling of the guide edge and result in uneven side register.

                                Remedy:
                                Adjust the alignment of the pusher plate. If the side guide mechanism is worn, have it repaired.

Cause C: Too much or too little clearance between the antibuckle plate and the sheet.

                                Remedy:
                                Set the antibuckle plate with a feeler gauge to give a clearance of about twice the thickness of the stock being printed up to a thickness of 0.010 in. (0.25 mm). For stocks thicker than 0.010 in., give a clearance of 0.005 in. (0.13 mm).

Cause D: The side guide touches the sheet before it has come to rest against the front guides.

                                Remedy 1:
                                Check and adjust the timing of the side guide and slow-down. This slow-down may prevent the sheets from reaching the front guides in time.

                                Remedy 2:
                                Correct the timing of the side guide.

Problem 7.   **Side guiding varies from sheet to sheet (pull side guide).**

Cause A: Improper guide setting.

                                Remedy:
                                Reset the side guide to the press manufacturer's specifications.

Cause B: Incorrect spring tension between the upper and lower guide rollers. Too little pressure will fail to pull all sheets firmly up to the stop and will cause irregular side register. Too much pressure will jam the edge of the sheet against the stop hard enough to buckle it, with similar results.

Remedy:
Find correct pressure for stock being printed by making trial settings. Thinner paper requires more accurate pressure. Use correct side guide spring for the paper being printed.

Cause C: Too little clearance for the sheet at the front guides, or any other obstruction that interferes with its side movement.

Remedy 1:
Adjust the clearance under the hold-down springs or fingers, and remove anything that obstructs easy side movement of the sheets.

Remedy 2:
Check sheet timing in relation to front stops.

NOTE: Many printers find a side-guide alarm to be a helpful addition to the press. The alarm alerts the press operator if the sheet is not properly guided.

Problem 8.   **Gripper edges of sheets are nicked or torn.**

Cause A: Too much gripper bite due to the improper adjustment of the front guides.

Remedy:
Set front guides back to reduce the gripper bite.

Cause B: Failure of front guides to clear the edge of the sheet as it starts forward, regardless of the method of insertion.

Remedy:
Check and adjust timing of the front guides.

Cause C: Improper synchronization in transferring sheets from one set of grippers to another anywhere from feed to delivery.

Remedy:
Clean, lubricate, and reset all gripper systems to produce proper gripper tension and travel times.

Problem 9.	**Wrinkles or creases.**
Cause A:	Paper not flat. (See Chapter 7, Problem 1.)
Cause B:	Paper slips out of one or more grippers while being held firmly by the others.

Remedy:
Clean and lubricate grippers and gripper pads.

Cause C: Grippers are not closing simultaneously, causing sheet distortion.

Position of wavy-edge wrinkle *(left)*

Position of tight-edge wrinkle *(right)*

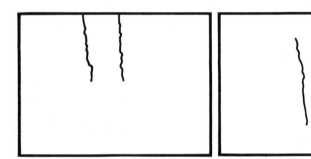

Remedy:
Have the manufacturer's representative correct faulty opening and closing timing. On modern presses, this is not a job for the press operator.

Cause D: Multiple front guides are out of line. The result is the same as if the paper had a bowed gripper edge.

Remedy:
Correct front guide alignment.

Cause E: Wheel tension or register table too tight.

Remedy:
Readjust wheel to minimum tension.

Problem 10. **Sheets pull out of grippers and stick to the blanket.**

Cause A: Tension on the grippers too weak to hold the paper against the pull of the ink. This is most likely to happen when large areas of solids are being printed. If the gripper tension is uneven, the sheets are pulled out of some grippers and torn.

Remedy:
Most gripper systems are cam closed. Check grippers for uniform timing and retime if necessary.

Cause B: Ink is excessively tacky.

Remedy 1:
Contact the inkmaker. Secure satisfactory ink.

Remedy 2:
Reduce the tack of the ink. (See Chapter 8, "Ink Problems.") ✓

Cause C: Blanket tacky with poor release.

Remedy:
Install a quick-release blanket. ✓

Cause D: Fast drying solvent swells the blanket making it tacky.

Remedy 1:
Contact the solvent supplier for a solvent that will not swell blankets.

Remedy 2:
Contact the ink manufacturer and make sure that the ink is ✓ not causing the problem.

Problem 11.   **Printed sheets are marked or smeared.**

Cause: Sheet transfer wheels are picking up wet ink from the sheets.

Remedy 1:
Move the transfer wheels to margins, nonimage, or light areas.

Remedy 2:
The transfer cylinder can be coated with a loose-fitting cheesecloth that has been chemically treated. This cheese-cloth, called "Super Blue," reduces transfer marking.

Remedy 3:
If the transfer cylinders are solid, weatherstripping or Velcron can be used to hold the wet surface of the print away from the cylinder.

Remedy 4:
Redesign the form to provide gutters.

Problem 12.   **Sheets fail to jog neatly.**

Cause A: Press moisture expands the printed side of the sheet, causing it to curl downward. Excessive moisture may cause thin sheets roll into tubes.

Remedy 1:
Reduce the plate moisture as much as possible. Alcohol or an alcohol substitute in the dampening solution will make it possible to use less moisture.

Remedy 2:
Use a sheet decurler.

NOTE: If these remedies don't solve the curling problem, contact the paper manufacturer. (See Chapter 7, "Paper Problems.")

Cause B: Printed sheets with a tail-end hook make the rear jogger ineffective. This condition results from heavy solids printed near the back edge. (See Chapter 7, "Problem 13.")

Remedy 1:
Reduce the tack of the ink.

Remedy 2:
Reduce the back-cylinder pressure to a minimum.

Remedy 3:
Avoid layouts that have solids near the back edge.

Remedy 4:
Change to a quick-release blanket.
Remedy 5:
Install a sheet decurler.

Cause C: Sheets falling short of the front stops or gate, or buckling as they strike the stops too hard.

Remedy:
Adjust the cam that controls the sheet release while the press is running at normal speed. If the press has slow-down devices, adjusting them is not critical, since the fingers will place the sheet properly.

Cause D: Rear vacuum slow-down rollers are plugged with spray powder and, therefore, are not controlling the sheets.

Remedy 1:
Clean the vacuum slow-down rollers.

Remedy 2:
Check the operation of the spray powder system.

Cause E: Static makes sheets stick together in the delivery.

Remedy 1:
Install a commercial static eliminator just before the press sheet is delivered.

Remedy 2:
Keep the pressroom RH above 35% RH. (Note "Cause D, Problem 1.")

2   Printing Unit Problems

The offset press printing unit consists of a plate cylinder, blanket cylinder, and impression cylinder geared together. Multicolor presses have two or more printing units in tandem, or plate and blanket cylinder couples arranged around a common impression cylinder. Blanket-to-blanket presses have no impression cylinder, and the blanket cylinder of each couple acts as the impression cylinder for the other.

Cylinder body with bearer

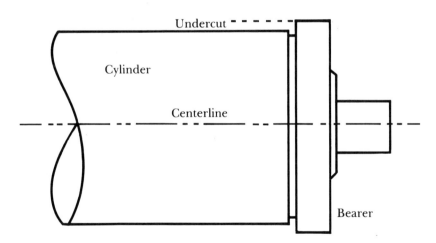

There are several press unit configurations in addition to the common equal-size cylinder arrangements. Some have double-size impression cylinders with two impression areas. One has a double-size impression cylinder with one impression area permitting double rolling of the plate and blanket before impression. Other presses are convertible, so that all units print on the same side of the sheet or some on one side and the rest on the other side.

A plate cylinder with plate clamps exposed

The printing press will function properly when the driving gears mesh and the plate and blanket are packed correctly. The cylinder bearers on most presses are meant to ensure accurate cylinder alignment and correct gear meshing, as well as serve as a guide for plate and blanket packing. Many presses require firm contact between plate and blanket cylinder bearers to smooth out the flow of power and prevent gear marking. Some presses, however, run without bearer contact.

Specifications for packing the plate and blanket are supplied with every offset press. If these have been lost, they should be replaced by the press manufacturer, the manufacturer's representative, or the manufacturer's successor. These specifications must be in the pressroom, and they must be used.

There is some flexibility in packing the plate and blanket. Packing sheets may be shifted from blanket to plate or vice versa without changing the squeeze pressure to lengthen or shorten the print from gripper to back edge. As a rule, no more than 0.005 in. (0.13 mm) of packing should be moved. Exceeding this amount can seriously damage the press. In folding carton work, print length should be adjusted on the step-and-repeat machine—not on the press.

It is important that the press cylinders be parallel and free from low spots. Low spots, even as shallow as 0.002 in. (0.05 mm), cause print quality problems. Low spots result from warping or from damage caused by passing debris, tools, and multiple sheets between the cylinders. Damaged cylinders cannot function properly and should be repaired.

The Ladder Target, a quality control test image available from the Graphic Arts Technical Foundation, is very helpful in the study of streaks, slurring, and doubling. The target is ¾ in. (19 mm) wide and 25 in. (635 mm) long and can be repeated to any length desired. While primarily designed for use by visual inspection, it has an area large enough to be read with a densitometer to provide numerical values. A full description of the target and its uses is given in GATF's Research Progress Report 99, *The GATF Ladder Target — A New Test Image.*

The principle problems of malfunctioning offset printing units with causes and remedies follow:

Problem 1:   **Gear streaks.** Gear streaks in printing are always parallel to the gripper edge of the sheets. Their pitch, or distance apart, is uniform and the same as the pitch of the cylinder's driving gear teeth.

Cause A: Incorrect plate and blanket diameters relative to the driving gear produces surface speed differences that cause slippage between the plate and blanket.

Improper packing of plate and blanket. The blanket is trying to drive the plate cylinder (i.e., it is fighting the gears). The problem is worse if there is not enough bearer pressure or if the gear teeth are worn.

Remedy:
Correct the plate and blanket packing. Start color jobs requiring more than one printing with the plate overpacked on the first unit and the blanket at or below bearer height. This allows more flexibility for shifting packing in succeeding passes, and the blanket will not work against the gears.

Cause B: Incorrect bearer pressure.

WARNING: Improper setting of bearer pressure can cause major damage to a press. Follow directions in the operating manual carefully.

Remedy:
Check the bearer pressure as follows:

1. Clean the bearers meticulously. Pack plate to correct printing height. Pack conventional blankets to 0.002–0.003 in. (0.050-0.075 mm) above correct printing height. Be sure that the blanket tension is correctly adjusted.

NOTE: Start with bearers backed off; then, gradually increase bearer pressure. Compressible blankets should not be used for this procedure.

2. Dab *light* ink thumbprints on blanket cylinder bearers in the gaps and in several places around the circumference.

3. Start the press and engage pressures for several revolutions; disengage pressures, and stop the machine.

4. Thumbprints should be transferred to plate cylinder bearers if bearer contact is correct.

An alternative method of checking bearer contact follows:

1. Clean bearers meticulously. With cylinders correctly packed, begin printing under normal conditions of speed, stock, and impression squeeze using a conventional blanket.

2. Carefully touch a glass-marking pencil to each blanket bearer for one or two revolutions until a continuous light ring of crayon is present.

3. Trip the press at operating speed, and examine the plate cylinder bearers. If bearer contact is correct, a similar complete ring of crayon will be present on the bearers. If the crayon transfer is only partial, then bearer contact is inadequate, or one or both of the cylinders are eccentric.
Use great care when setting bearer pressures. Presses that have sleeve bushings are susceptible to damage from excessive bearer pressure; the bushings can heat up and score or seize. Several European presses are manufactured with this bushing design. Presses that have double ball or taper roller bearings may require an increase in bearing preload before bearer contact is set. Where specialized help is not readily available, specific instructions should be sought from the manufacturer or agent before proceeding.

Cause C: Accumulation of fibers and dirt cause gear teeth to bottom.

Remedy:
Clean the gear teeth.

Cause D: Worn cylinder bearings.

Remedy:
If remedies for Causes A, B, and C do not help, have the worn bearings checked and adjusted or replaced. Occasionally, gear streaking can be reduced by using compressible blankets.

Cause E: Ink too soft or greasy.

Remedy:
Use a stiffer ink. Sometimes gear streaks can be seen on the blanket during a run but not on the sheet. This signals the problems previously outlined. When greasy, soft, or "soupy" ink is used, the streaks are amplified, becoming visible on the sheet.

Problem 2.   **Nongear streaks.** Streaks other than gear streaks may be parallel to the gripper edge or from front to back. If they run from front to back, they bear no relation to the pitch of the gear teeth.

Cause: Nongear streaks due to malfunctioning ink rollers, dampening rollers, or a slipping blanket.

Remedies:
See Chapter 3, "Horizontal streaks," and Chapter 6, "Horizontal streaks in printing." If the streaking pattern is irregular or variable, check for correct tensioning of fitted main motor drive belts. There should be no oil or grease on the drive belts.

Problem 3.   **Uneven impression.** Uneven color can result from two conditions—uneven or varying ink feed, and uneven cylinder pressures. Ink feeding problems are covered in Chapter 3. The causes of uneven pressures follow.

Cause A: The plate, blanket, or impression cylinder is dented or warped. To check these cylinders:

1. Remove the plate and packing.

2. Check roundness with a dial indicator.

Remedy:
Have the cylinder repaired by the manufacturer or a press mechanic.

Cause B: Blanket not uniform in thickness. ✓

Blankets should be monitored for consistency and uniformity. Use a dead-weight bench micrometer. All areas can be reached by rolling the blanket in the throat of the gauge.

As an alternative method:

1. Be sure that the plate cylinder is parallel. (See Cause A.)

2. Put a plate on the press, and pack it to bearer height.

3. Pack the blanket to 0.001 in. (0.025 mm) above bearers.

4. Ink up the dry plate, and pull an impression on the blanket; note the bare areas.

5. Turn the blanket end for end, wash it clean, and pull another ink impression on it. If the bare areas are now in different places, the blanket is at fault.

6. Make sure blanket tensioning is not excessive. Use a torque wrench.

Remedy 1:
Replace the blanket with a new one.

Remedy 2:
As a stopgap measure, use an aerosol adhesive to patch the back of the blanket in the low areas with tissues torn to the required shape.

Cause C: Blanket cylinder dented or warped. To check for this, first be sure that the plate cylinder is parallel (see Cause A), and then put a new blanket on the blanket cylinder. Follow the procedure under Cause B through item 4. If the bare area remains in the same place after the blanket has been reversed, the blanket cylinder is dented or warped.

Remedy:
Have the cylinder replaced or repaired by the manufacturer
or a press mechanic.

Cause D: Impression cylinder dented or warped. To check for this, first
be sure that the plate and blanket cylinders are parallel and
that the blanket is free from low spots. (See Causes A, B, and
C.) Next, roll up the blanket with a thin film of ink, and
bring up the impression cylinder a little at a time until ink
just begins to transfer. The ink will not transfer to depres-
sions in the cylinder.

Remedy 1:
Have the impression cylinder replaced or repaired by the
press manufacturer or a press mechanic.

Remedy 2:
Build up the dented or warped impression cylinder by
metal spraying; then, have it reground or polished.
For a long-lasting repair of an uneven impression
cylinder, use the following procedure.

1. When A, B, and C (above) have been completed, pull a
moderately inked solid on enamel paper at low impression
pressure to show cylinder low spots.

2. Carefully cut out the low spots from the printed sheet.

3. Meticulously clean all ink, oil, and grease from the impression cylinder. The solvent used should dry without leaving a
deposit.

4. Pass the cut sheet into the press, stopping when the sheet
is against the impression cylinder.

5. Using the cut sheet as a template, spray the cylinder with
one or two light coats of automobile body zinc primer.

6. When the primer is dry, repeat the light solid print on
paper, cut out low spots, and respray in the same manner
until the low spots are built up.

7. When the buildup is completely dry, the paint edges

caused by the template can be smoothed with rubbing compound.

An impression cylinder that has been dented locally by running of a small object such as a screw, spring, or allen wrench through the press can be repaired as follows.

1. Drill a hole in the indentation, tap, and insert a soft metal screw dipped in a thread sealant such as Loctite. Saw or clip off the head and excess thread close to the cylinder.

2. Drill another hole slightly overlapping the first repair and repeat step 1. Continue until the impression of the object has been covered.

3. Carefully file the excess material until very close to the surface of the cylinder.

4. Using a small oilstone, polish the repair down to cylinder level. Extreme caution is required in order not to recess the repair below the cylinder radius.

This procedure is only practical when damage is confined to the area of the article passing between the cylinders. The cylinder must be removed if it has dished around the indentation. This is a delicate repair operation and should be done by a skilled press mechanic.

Cause E: Plate and blanket cylinders not parallel, or plate and impression cylinders not parallel.

Remedy:
Check the press operating manual, or call a repair technician to make the cylinders parallel.

Cause F: "Gap ghosts," an area of light impression corresponding in width to approximately the width of the cylinder gap. As a pair of cylinders enter their gap areas during printing, wear in bearings, eccentrics, or simply lack of good bearer contact can cause the bearing pressure on the third cylinder to relax somewhat.

Remedy 1:
Adjust or replace cylinder bearings.

Remedy 2:
Increase bearer contact between plate and blanket cylinders.

Remedy 3:
On older presses that may not be economically overhauled, use compressible blankets. This remedy can occasionally reduce the problem.

Remedy 4:
Use a different press. Avoid using worn-out presses for critical jobs.

Cause G: Dirty cylinder bearers. Dirt on one bearer lifts that end of the cylinder, reducing the pressure.

Remedy:
Keep bearers clean at all times.

Problem 4. **Slur or slurring.**

Cause A: Incorrect plate and blanket packing. Where a significant difference in peripheral speed occurs between plate and blanket, the elasticity of the blanket will allow it to move and distort in the plate-to-blanket nip area when lubricated by the inked image areas. (See Chapter 7, Problem 6.)

Remedy:
Use a good grade of packing paper to pack the plate and blanket according to manufacturer's specifications.

Cause B: Too much back-cylinder pressure in printing on coated papers. Slur shows up on shadow tones, filling in images and causing loss of detail. Highlights usually are unaffected.

Remedy 1:
Run with a minimum of back-cylinder pressure. Run strong inks as spare as possible.

Remedy 2:
Use a compressible blanket.

Cause C: Too much plate-to-blanket pressure when running a smooth or lightly grained plate.

Remedy:
Reduce plate-to-blanket squeeze to a minimum. Ungrained plates need no more than about 0.003 in. (0.075 mm) of impression when using conventional blankets or 0.005–0.006 in. (0.13–0.15 mm) when using compressible blankets.

Cause D: Running too much ink on coated stock.

Remedy:
Reduce ink feed. If this reduces color or black density, reduce the water feed. If necessary, use a small amount of alcohol or alcohol substitute in the dampening solution to reduce the ink required. Less ink is needed when the plate is not very moist. An alternative is to run less of a stronger ink.

Cause E: Ink rollers set too hard, or tight ink roller bearing. Either condition can cause an ink form roller to drag on the plate.

Remedy:
Release roller settings, spin form rollers to check for freeness, and reset correctly.

Cause F: Blanket tension is insufficient.

Remedy:
Use a torque wrench to correct blanket tension effectively on most presses. The torque wrench needed depends on the blanket and press. Make sure all units are corrected to the same blanket tension.

Cause G: Paper coating piling on the printing areas of the blanket. This piling usually starts in the midtones on the second or a later unit of a multicolor press and produces a mottled pattern due to slurred dots.

Remedy 1:
Add some wetting agent to the dampening solution.

Remedy 2:
Switch to a more moisture resistant coated stock. (See Chapter 7, Problem 17, and Chapter 8, Problem 16.)

Problem 5.   **Marking of the printed sheet.**

Cause A: Marking occurs (on the front side of the sheet) when the wet image contacts or "slaps" the transfer cylinder. On multicolor presses, often the sheet being stripped from the blanket is immediately transported by a transfer cylinder.

Remedy 1:
Use a commercial transfer cylinder treatment (called Super Blue) with a loose, coated cheesecloth to support the sheet.

Remedy 2:
In most presses, cover the transfer cylinder with a coarse, random-pattern material such as the glass-beaded or carborundum-coated fabric used on steps to prevent slipping. Be sure that there is adequate clearance between the transfer and adjacent cylinders and that the material used is firmly bonded to the cylinder. In machines with disks or star wheels, the sheet layout should incorporate gutters or trim areas in which these wheels can run. Where this precaution has not been observed, cord or piano wire tightly drawn between two extreme disk wheels is occasionally effective.

Cause B: Sheets rippling as they enter the impression nip, contacting the blanket prematurely in some areas. This rippling, which happens if the paper is not flat, has the appearance of a light double image immediately adjacent to the desired image. Such marking occurs in isolated areas of the sheet rather than over the whole sheet.

Remedy 1:
Check sheet insertion relative to the feedboard setup (i.e., sheet timing, side guide adjustments, insertion pad bar height).

Remedy 2:
Replace the stock.

Remedy 3:
Tighten the paper hold-down brush on the impression cylinder. This recommendation applies to single-color presses and the first unit of multicolor presses. On the later units of a multicolor press, it may be necessary to use the hold-down air blasts or electrostatic hold-down devices.

Remedy 4:
Recondition the paper to reduce waviness or tight edges.

Problem 6.   **Doubling on multicolor press.** Doubling is a special case of misregister. On multicolor presses, an ink image is transferred from the sheet onto nonimage areas of the blanket of the next unit. These images print back onto the following sheets. Unless this print-back is in exact register with the original print, a double is produced. Doubling is particularly objectionable in halftones since it varies from sheet to sheet, causing up-and-down variations in color values.

Cause A: Sheets slipping in grippers. If a sheet slips slightly in the grippers, the print-back from the following blanket is out of register, causing a double and increasing color value. Such slippage varies between sheets, producing different colors.

Remedy 1:
Make sure grippers are clean and operate freely.

Remedy 2:
Adjust impression and transfer cylinder grippers, making sure tension is sufficient and uniform.

Remedy 3:
Check for end play in the gripper shaft, wear in the shaft bushings, and return-spring strength where fitted. Any failings should be corrected.

Remedy 4:
Check for cam runner wear. The runner surface should be smooth, and the runner free from radial play. A small amount of side play is acceptable on some runners.

Remedy 5:
Check for worn cams. The operating lobes of cams should not have burrs or sharp edges. If they do, replace them.

Remedy 6:
Reduce the ink tack on the unit where slipping is occurring. This unit is likely to be printing the largest solid areas.

Cause B: Play in impression or transfer cylinders, end play, torsional flexing, or worn bearings or bushings.

Remedy:
Have the press overhauled and worn parts replaced.

Cause C: Mechanical disturbances. Doubling from mechanical sources other than gripper slip frequently exhibits a sequential pattern (e.g., on every second or every third sheet).

Remedy:
This is a problem for a press mechanic. Consult the press manufacturer. Investigate machine functions that harmonize with the doubling pattern. These include one set of grippers on a two- or three-gripper transfer cylinder, dampening feed motion, ink feed motion, or ink oscillation motion. If possible, stop each oscillating motion to see if the doubling condition changes. Then, have any affected part repaired. Where one set of transfer grippers might be the problem, carefully attach a small piece of felt to the side of a gripper pad on the transfer cylinder, and moisten it with marking ink so that sheets are marked as they pass through. Resume printing for at least thirty sheets; then, check the relationship of the doubled sheet to the marked sheet. This inspection will identify the faulty part, which should be repaired or replaced.

Cause D: Wavy- or tight-edged paper distorted in the impression. Unfortunately, no sheet will be distorted in exactly the same way in successive impressions. Furthermore, no two sheets will be distorted in the same way by the same printing unit. As a result, the pickup of all but the final color will vary in position on the succeeding blankets, producing doubles and variable halftone color values.

Remedy 1:
Keep paper tightly wrapped until ready to use. Wrap any paper that is to be sent back to storage.

Remedy 2:
Wrap delivery piles with a plastic cover.

Remedy 3:
Control the relative humidity of the pressroom.

Remedy 4:
Replace the paper.

Cause E: Multiple-sheeted paper. Occasionally, a sequential double
can be caused by paper that has been sheeted several rolls at
a time when one of the rolls has different characteristics
from the rest.

Remedy:
Insert 15 to 20 sheets of similar stock from another manufacturer into the feeder and check for a change in the double
when it is passed through.

3   Ink Feed and Distribution Problems

The inking system of an offset printing unit usually consists of an ink fountain, fountain roller, ductor roller, three or four metal oscillating (vibrating) rollers, four or more rubber intermediate rollers, and three or four form rollers made from synthetic rubber or other polymer. The ink fountain and ductor rollers feed the ink in controlled amounts. The oscillators and intermediate rollers distribute the ink onto the form roller in a uniform, thin film, then work the ink into printing consistency. The form rollers apply the ink to the plate image according to its requirements.

A typical inking system

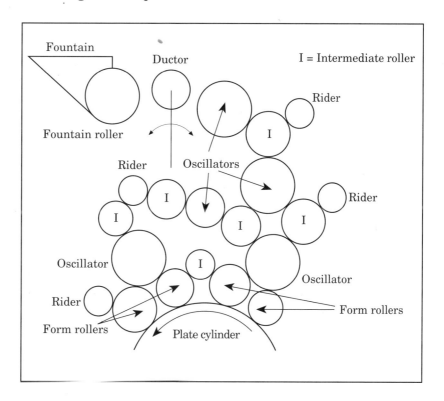

In order to function properly, the oscillating rollers must be driven by gears or chains and have the same surface speed as the printing plate. The ductor, intermediate, and form rollers are driven by surface contact only. The fountain roller is driven intermittently by an adjustable pawl and ratchet or clutch. Setting the fountain blade and moving the fountain roller determines the amount of ink delivered to the rollers and eventually to the printed sheets.

Uniform distribution of ink around the rollers results from the differing diameters of the rollers and oscillators. Circumferential roller distribution is produced by oscillation of the vibrating rollers, which is usually adjustable. Ink film thickness lengthwise of the rollers is not necessarily uniform, since the requirements of the form may vary considerably across the press. Such local requirements are met by adjusting the flexible or segmented fountain blade.

Ink problems are comprehensively discussed in two GATF textbooks—*What the Printer Should Know about Ink* and *Solving Offset Ink Problems.*

Some common inking system problems follow.

Problem 1.   **Horizontal streaks.** Roller streaks are always parallel to the gripper edge of the sheets. Unlike gear streaks, however, they have no relationship to the pitch of the cylinder drive gear teeth. There may be only one streak or several streaks spaced at varying or equal distances.

Cause A: Gear Streaks. (See "Gear Streaks" in Chapter 2.)

Cause B: One or more form rollers are set too tightly against the plate. The form rollers strike the leading edge of the plate and bounce. This action ruptures the ink film from end to end, producing a streak on the roller that is transferred to the plate after one revolution. Such streaks are worse if all form rollers are the same size and if all are set too tightly against the plate. Gear streaking is most objectionable on background color tints.

Remedy:
Reset form rollers to proper pressure against plate and oscillator.

Cause C: Too much end play in form rollers permits them to move horizontally with the oscillating rollers. If the form rollers are on the plate when the oscillating roller reverses, they may slip horizontally and produce streaks.

Remedy 1:
Adjust form roller sockets to eliminate end play. If necessary, place washers on the roller spindles.

Strip method of roller setting

Remedy 2:
Adjust the timing of the oscillator so that the direction reversal occurs while the form rollers are opposite the plate cylinder gap. This adjustment, which can be done on some presses, should eliminate streaks caused by end play.

Cause D: Skidding form rollers. Rollers set with unequal pressure against the oscillator and plate cause this condition. If settings are unequal, the roller will skid on the surface where the setting is lighter, producing streaks. Skidding is more likely to occur if the rollers are glazed.

Remedy 1:
Reset the form rollers with less pressure to the plate than to the oscillator.

Remedy 2:
Recondition the form rollers and oscillating rollers to remove glaze. Glaze is due to the accumulation of dried ink and gum that was not removed by ordinary washup solvents. Use a glaze-removing washup material.

Picture method of roller setting

Cause E: A loose and slipping blanket. Because it is frequently necessary to lengthen or shorten the print, the surface speed of the plate and blanket are not always equal. If the blanket is loose, it may tend to follow the plate and slip on the blanket cylinder. This intermittent slippage causes streaks. Slippage increases as plate-to-blanket pressure increases.

Remedy:
Tighten the blanket. Use the packing gauge to check the plate-to-blanket pressure and, if too high, remove the excess packing.

Cause F: Worn or mismatched drive belts. If one belt becomes frayed or stretched more than the other(s), the resulting uneven surges of power can cause streaks.

Remedy:
Replace with a complete set of matched belts.

Problem 2.

Ink feeds unevenly. Ink is fed by intermittent rotation of the fountain roller. The ink feed is controlled by setting the flexible fountain blade, which allows the amount of ink to vary across the press according to the demands of the plate; and the varying rotation of the fountain roller, which governs the amount of ink fed to all areas. The ductor roller alternates between contacting the fountain roller and the upper ink oscillator. It transfers a streak of fresh ink to the oscillator. This ink is worked out to a smooth film by the time it reaches the form rollers. The lateral motion of the oscillators tends to spread the ink uniformly from side to side across the press. However, oscillation can be adjusted to deliver the necessary amount of ink to all areas. Lateral distribution is reduced to a minimum when operating with two or more colors in a split fountain.

Cause A:

Stripping of ink rollers. This is the result of glazed rollers, too much dampening solution, or too much gum or phosphoric acid, or both in the dampening solution. The rollers become saturated with water and fail to take or transfer ink, which results in the inability to maintain color. Generally, it is the metal oscillators that strip, but if rubber rollers become glazed, they too can strip.

Remedy 1:
Wash up the press by using a two-step (or three-step) washup method.

Remedy 2:
If only the metal oscillators are stripping, wash the system free from ink, remove the form and intermediate rollers, and scrub the metal oscillators thoroughly.

Remedy 3:
If rubber rollers strip, remove the glaze by scrubbing them. (Caution: Wear goggles, rubber gloves, and a rubber apron.) As another solution, these rollers can be reground on a lathe to remove the glaze.

Remedy 4:
Since the metal oscillators are the principal cause of stripping, remove them and electroplate them with copper, or have them covered with ebonite or Teflon. These materials strongly resist stripping.

Remedy 5:
To avoid removing the metal oscillators, which involves partially dismantling the press, chemically copperize them on the press. Such copper plating is very thin and may wear off in a week to six months, but it is easy to renew.

Cause B: Ink "backing away" from the fountain roller, thereby reducing the ink feed. Actually, the ink does not back away; it simply sets up in the fountain and fails to flow down to the fountain roller. Such an ink may be too short, too thixotropic, or too cold.

Remedy 1:
Work the ink in the fountain frequently to keep it fluid.

Remedy 2:
Install a mechanical ink fountain agitator.

Remedy 3:
Obtain a longer, more fluid ink.

A mechanical ink agitator
Courtesy of Baldwin Gegenheimer Div.

Remedy 4:
Raise the pressroom temperature. Most inks work best at 75–80°F (21–24°C).

Cause C: Ink building, caking, or piling on the roller surfaces and on the image areas of the plate and blanket. With this condition, the ink fails to transfer properly, resulting in loss of color. Piling may be due to incompletely dispersed pigment or to waterlogging of the ink. (See Chapter 6, Problem 17 and Chapter 8, Problem 16.)

Remedy 1:
Check the degree of pigment dispersion in the ink with a fineness-of-grind gauge. If the test shows many coarse particles or aggregates, have the ink reground.

Remedy 2:
Reduce the plate moisture to a minimum. If this corrective action does not help, add a small amount of water-resistant varnish to the ink, or get an ink that resists waterlogging.

Fineness-of-grind gauge

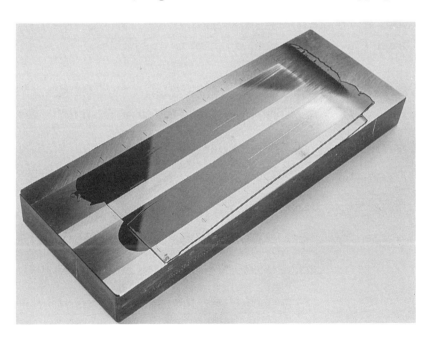

Cause D: Ink rollers or blanket fouled with lint from the paper. Lint, being cellulose fibers, absorbs water, becomes ink repellent, and refuses to transfer a continuous ink film.

Remedy 1:
Wash all ink off the rollers using the washup attachment. Hand-wash the rollers to remove the lint.

Remedy 2:
Reduce the ink tack.

Remedy 3:
Obtain paper that has a minimum linting tendency.

Remedy 4:
Install a sheet cleaner.

Cause E: Low spots in rollers prevent uniform contact between them or between form rollers and plate.

Remedy 1:
Replace defective rollers.

Remedy 2:
Remove the defective rollers and have them reground.

Cause F: Bent roller cores or spindles.

Remedy:
Remove the defective rollers and have their coverings removed. Have the cores or spindles repaired and re-covered.

Cause G: Bent or unevenly worn fountain blade with a scalloped edge. This condition prevents accurate setting.

Remedy:
Obtain a new, straight fountain blade. When installing it, be sure that the ink fountain keys are backed off and turn freely. Use the keys and a feeler gauge to adjust the blade according to the press manufacturer's instructions, usually to a clearance of 0.012–0.020 in. (0.3–0.5 mm). Once the blade is parallel to the ink fountain roller, make further adjustments according to job requirements. Never force the blade against the fountain roller; to do so would cause uneven wear. When tightening the blade overall, start by turning the screws at the center and work toward the ends. When opening up the blade gap, start at both ends and work toward the center.

Cause H: Accumulation of dirt or dried ink between the fountain blade and roller interferes with the ink feed.

Remedy:
Keep the blade and roller clean at all times.

Cause I: Dried ink and solvent left on the ends of the rollers by the washup attachment causes rubber form roller ends to blister, swell, or peel. The result is ink emulsification and poor inking along the sides of the plate.

Remedy:
When the machine washup is completed and the press is idle, always wipe the ends of the rollers until dry. Rollers that have become damaged should be replaced.

4 Plate Dampening Problems

Many offset presses are equipped with the conventional dampening system, a water fountain (water pan), fountain roller, ductor roller, distributing roller (oscillator), and two dampening form rollers.

The fountain (water pan) roller is partly immersed in the dampening solution and rotates slowly. On many presses, its speed varies with the press speed, but the present trend is toward an independent variable-speed drive. The roller is chrome or aluminum and may be bare or covered with a muslin sleeve.

The conventional ductor roller is covered with molleton or other suitable fabric. It alternates between contacting the fountain roller and distributing roller. Its dwell time on the fountain roller is adjustable and, if the speed of the fountain roller varies with the press speed, the dwell time controls the amount of moisture fed to the dampening rollers. A fountain roller with a variable-speed drive also controls water feed and makes finer adjustment possible. The water-distributing, or oscillating, roller is made of aluminum or chrome. The surface speed of this roller is the same as that of the press plate when packed to the specified height.

At first, dampening form rollers were steel cores covered by sleeves or undercovers of coarse wool flannel with sleeves of molleton or a similar textile on top of the wool. The first important change was the use of a rubber-covered core omitting the flannel underlayer. This is called a "bareback" roller. The use of a parchment paper sleeve on special dampening rollers was the next important development. Parchment paper covers are easily replaced and can be changed whenever necessary. The popular 3M sleeve is a further improvement on parchment paper sleeves.

Most presses sold today are equipped with a brush dampener or a continuous-feed contact dampener. The various designs are classified and reviewed in a series of articles by John MacPhee (*Graphic Arts Monthly,* April 1981, p. 35; September 1984, p. 75; October 1984, p. 75; and November 1984, p. 86).

The newer dampening systems give more precise control and respond much more rapidly to changes in press settings than did the old systems with cloth-covered rollers.

A conventional dampening system that uses covered form and ductor rollers

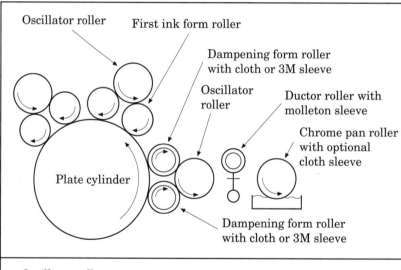

A conventional dampening system that uses a bareback form roller

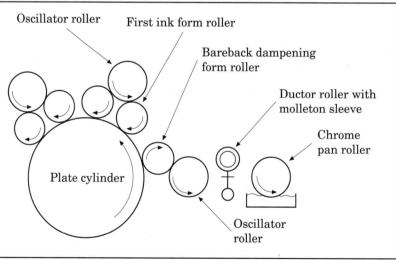

Epic Litho/Dampener
plate-feed
dampening system

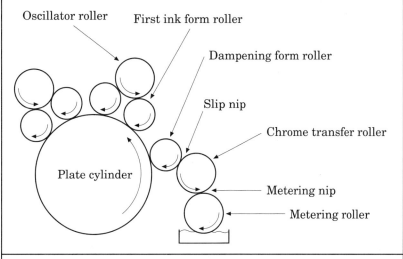

Roland-Matic
plate-feed
continuous-feed
dampening system

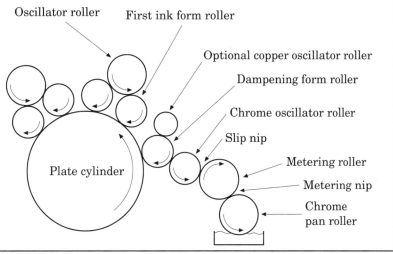

Miller-Meter
plate-feed
continuous-feed
dampening system

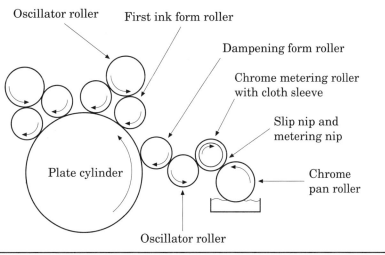

Two configurations
of the Dahlgren
inker-feed
dampening system

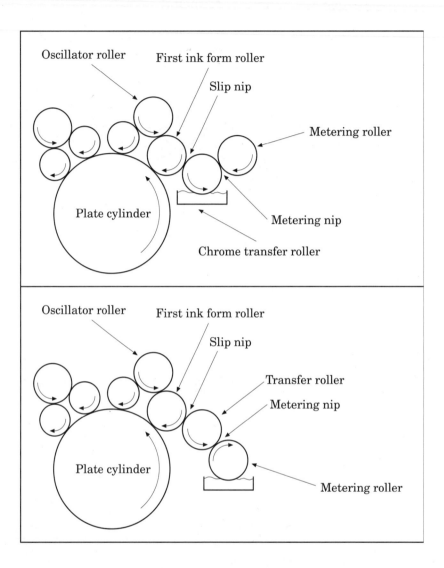

Developments of better dampening systems and improved
lithographic plates have greatly reduced emulsification,
wash marks, ink drying, and roller stripping from too much
dampening solution, and scum and catchup from too little
dampening solution. The following press problems result
from too much or too little dampening.

Problem 1:   **Wash marks.**

Cause: Wash marks are streaks around the plate, blanket, and print
caused by too much dampening water. The ink doesn't absorb

the excess water. If the water control is so critical that it leaves little margin between wash marks and scumming, the plate is poorly desensitized or the ink is too water-repellent.

Remedy 1:
Reduce the water feed or reduce dampener speed. Add alcohol or an alcohol substitute to the dampening solution.

Remedy 2:
Check the hardness of rubber rollers. Replace rollers that are too hard.

Remedy 3:
Have the plate remade.

Remedy 4:
Get a better ink.

Problem 2.

Snowflaky solids. Black solids are gray, and colored solids are weak. Under a glass, they appear uneven and full of tiny white specks.

Cause A:

Too much dampening water. The ink absorbs the excess water. When the ink film is split on the plate or blanket, water droplets are exposed. These droplets prevent a uniform solid from transferring to the paper.

Remedy 1:
Reduce the water feed. Add alcohol or an alcohol substitute.

Remedy 2:
If the ink on the rollers appears to be waterlogged, change to an ink that is less water receptive.

Remedy 3:
Install a system to blow low-pressure air on the back side of the inking system. This evaporates water from the ink.

Cause B:

Inadequate plate-to-blanket, blanket-to-substrate, and/or roller-to-plate pressure.

Remedy:
Check packing and roller settings. Correct to manufacturer's specifications.

Problem 3. **Color variation.** This problem can be caused by ink rollers stripping, ink "backing away" from the fountain roller, ink piling on the ink rollers, or paper lint and dust fouling the ink. Some other causes are low spots in rollers, bent roller cores or spindles, and dirt or dried ink between the fountain blade and roller. These problems are described at length elsewhere in this book. If none of these causes apply, consider the following:

Cause: Varying feed of the dampening solution.

Remedy:
Maintain a constant level of solution in the water fountain. Water fountain levelers are available for this purpose.

Problem 4. **Scum streaks around the cylinder.** Scum streaks are usually due to inadequate moisture or excessive plate wear.

Cause A: Dirty or worn dampener or ductor roller covers, greasy fountain roller, or greasy distributing roller. These conditions prevent uniform dampening across the press.

Remedy:
If the dampener or ductor roller covers are dirty, wash them to remove ink accumulations. If they are threadbare, replace them. If the fountain and distributing rollers are greasy and fail to hold continuous films of water, scrub them with naphtha; then, etch them, drying down the etch.

Cause B: Nonuniform pressure of dampening rollers against the plate causes uneven wear.

Remedy 1:
Reset dampening rollers, making sure the pressure is uniform from end to end. After the rollers have been set, make sure they are never reversed.

Remedy 2:
Check dampeners for alignment. If the spindle or core of the roller is bent, it should be repaired and the roller re-covered.

Problem 5. **Scum streaks across the plate.** Such streaks, like those around the cylinder, are usually due to insufficient moisture or excessive plate wear.

Cause: Dampening rollers set too tightly against the plate. When they strike the leading edge of the plate, they bounce. The bump causes rapid wear of the plate's front edge, producing a scum streak. It also squeezes excess moisture onto the plate in a line from end to end on the dampeners. This excess in turn causes a water streak just one revolution of the roller back from the leading edge.

Remedy:
Reset the dampening rollers to the proper pressure.
(For other causes of scum streaks across the plate, see Chapter 3, "Ink Feeding and Distribution Problems.")

Problem 6.   **Plate scums after 10,000-20,000 impressions.**

Cause: Insufficient acid or gum or both in the dampening solution.

Remedy 1:
Check the dampening solution concentration. This requires the use of a conductivity meter.

A Myron L meter used to measure conductivity and pH

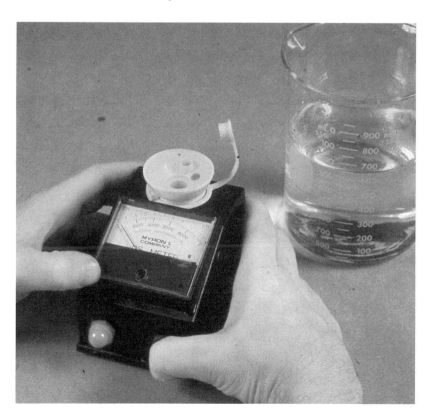

Remedy 2:
Remake the dampening solution, carefully following the manufacturer's instructions.

Remedy 3:
Consult the dampening solution supplier.

(For other causes of plate scumming, see Chapter 5, "Plate and Press Problems.")

Problem 7.   **Halftones sharpen and highlight dots are lost during the pressrun.**

Cause: Too much acid in dampening solution.

Remedy 1:
Have the plate remade.

Remedy 2:
Check the pH value of the dampening solution. Acid solutions should be 4.0-5.0. If the dampening solution is too acidic, change it. Once highlight dots have been lost, they cannot be brought back. (For other causes of image failure, see Chapter 5, "Plate and Press Problems.")

Problem 8.   **Fiber-shaped white spots.** Fiber-shaped white spots in printed solids are the result of cellulose fibers adhering to the plate or the blanket. Such fibers absorb moisture until they become saturated, after which time they repel ink and print reverse images of themselves.

Cause A: Lint, fluff, or whiskers picked up from paper or board.

Remedy:
See Chapter 7, "Paper Problems."

Cause B: Fibers released from molleton or other fiber dampening-roller covers. These covers eventually begin to shed their nap fibers because of wear or mildew. Nap fibers can be distinguished from paper fibers, because they are from two to four times as long. They can also be identified by laboratory tests.

Remedy 1:
Re-cover the dampener and ductor rollers.

Remedy 2:
Use parchment paper dampener covers. These are replaced frequently and do not shed fibers.

Remedy 3:
Install one of the newer dampening systems that do not require roller covers.

Problem 9.   **Metering roller or chrome roller scums or accepts ink.**

Cause A: Dampening solution failure.

Remedy 1:
Discard the dampening solution, and prepare a fresh solution carefully following directions and measuring the ingredients.

Remedy 2:
Secure a different dampening solution.

Cause B: Improperly set dampening system.

Remedy:
Check all settings and correct them to manufacturer's specifications.

Cause C: Improper amount of isopropyl alcohol or alcohol substitute.

Remedy 1:
Check the alcohol concentration with a hydrometer, and correct if necessary.

Remedy 2:
Buy an alcohol control system.

Cause D: Poor cleaning procedures.

Remedy:
Clean the press carefully, and keep it clean.

Problem 10.   **Plate dries up on gear side.**

Cause A: Excess pressure between rollers on gear side.

Remedy:
Adjust feed on gear side to allow more dampening solution to flow to the plate.

Cause B: Metering roller improperly skewed.

Remedy:
Increase the skew of the metering roller.

Cause C: Air blowing on the press.

Remedy:
Eliminate drafts from open windows, doors, or fans.

Problem 11.   **Plate wet in the center.**

Cause A: Metering roller improperly skewed.

Remedy:
Increase the skew on the metering roller.

Cause B: Chrome roller improperly adjusted.

Remedy:
Set the chrome to form roller nip correctly.

Cause C: Damaged or worn metering roller.

Remedy:
Check the metering roller for damage. Check its diameter and roundness. Repair or replace if necessary.

Problem 12.   **Water drops falling on sheets.**

Cause A: Condensation on dampening system.

Remedy 1:
Repair insulation on dampening solution pans.

Remedy 2:
Increase dampening solution temperature.

Cause B: Dampening solution thrown from metering roller.

Remedy:
Remove the dried-ink cuffs at the ends of the rollers.
Keep rollers adequately cleaned.

Problem 13.   **Foaming in dampening system.**

Cause A: Insufficient alcohol or defoamer.

Remedy:
Check alcohol concentration with a hydrometer, and correct
the amount if necessary.

Cause B: Excess gum in the dampening solution.

Remedy:
Discard the dampening solution, and prepare a fresh solution carefully measuring the ingredients and following
directions.

Cause C: Improperly installed filters on alcohol control system.

Remedy:
Check the filters, and install them correctly.

Cause D: Excess pressure on return side of alcohol control system.

Remedy:
Reduce the return flow rate. Restrict flow with a valve or
with a flow restrictor.

Cause E: Soap or surfactant in the dampening solution.

Remedy 1:
Clean automatic dampening system carefully by hand.

Remedy 2:
Be sure molleton covers are thoroughly rinsed after washing.

Remedy 3:
Check to see if the alcohol substitute promotes foaming, and
add defoamer or replace it if necessary.

Problem 14.   **Water forms bands on the dampening rollers and the
plate.**

Cause A: Metering roller too hard.

Remedy:
Check the hardness of the metering roller, and replace it if necessary. Softer metering rollers are needed when running alcohol substitutes.

Cause B: Chrome roller improperly set.

Remedy:
Set the chrome roller correctly against the form roller.

Cause C: Worn gears.

Remedy:
Check the gears on the metering and chrome rollers. Replace them if necessary.

5   Plate and Press Problems

The lithographic press plate differs from other mechanical printing plates in that it is planographic. Its image and nonimage areas are essentially on the same level. The image areas are not raised as in letterpress and flexography, nor depressed as in gravure printing. Image areas are ink-receptive and surrounded by nonimage, water-receptive areas. When the plate is moistened and inked, the water-receptive areas refuse to take ink while the image areas repel the water and accept the ink.

Great improvements have been made in offset plates since the 1950s. The press operator is no longer required to be a plate expert. Plates are expected to work when they are delivered to the press, and they usually do. Plate problems (blinding, scumming, and premature image wear) have been greatly diminished by major, technical advances.

Lithographic plates are coated with a light-sensitive coating. (Presensitized plates are coated by the manufacturer; wipe-on plates are coated by the printer.) When exposed to light, the coating is changed so that the plate processor removes the coating in the nonimage area.

Most plates are made of paper or aluminum, although some bimetal plates are used for long runs and jobs that are repeated (e.g., greeting cards or books).

Negative-working plates must be treated with a coating that hardens or becomes insoluble when exposed to light. After exposing the plates under a negative film, the processor removes the unexposed coating, and this area becomes the nonimage area.

Positive-working plates are treated with a coating that becomes soluble upon exposure to light. When developed, the unexposed area becomes the image area.

Overexposing negative-working plates causes halftone dot gain, while overexposing positive-working plates causes halftone dots to sharpen or shrink.

Most plates used in the United States and Canada are negative-working. Using negatives is easy and may save film. Negative-working plates are often faster to process and permit easier multiple exposures. They also do not require cleanup of film-edge and tape marks.

Positive-working plates can be treated to give longer runs, permit easier register control, and provide more flexibility of midtone and highlight control. Positive-working plates are commonly used in most European and Asian countries.

Presensitized plates may be "additive" or "subtractive." *Additive* plates have an image-reinforcing material which is added during processing. The image-reinforcing material on *subtractive* plates is applied during manufacture, and the unexposed coating, including the image-reinforcing material, is removed from the nonimage area during processing.

New technology has created many excellent plate choices for the printer. It is imperative, however, that the printer use only procedures and chemicals recommended by the plate manufacturer.

• A plate that can be used with positive or negative film is available. The developer removes the exposed coating from the plates exposed to the positive film, or it removes the unexposed coating from the plates exposed to the negative film. The printer can stock only one kind of plate for both processes.

• Life of positive- or negative-working plates can be extended by post-treatment. Positive-working plates that are baked (in excess of 480°F or 249°C) are suitable for runs in excess of one million copies. Some negative plates can also be baked. Some negative-working plates can be post-exposed (after developing) to extend the plate life as much as four-fold.

• Some special plates are heat-treated prior to development, which increases the run length.

• Most plants use plate processors on plates for all presses—from the duplicator to the largest commercial press.

• Anodized plates are produced by giving aluminum plates a special surface that, under a scanning electron microscope, looks like a honeycomb. Gum and coating material adhere better to the anodized surface, and the plate is more resistant to abrasion, wear, and chemical attack.

There are many different plates, and the printer has many choices. Choosing the right plate is important. The run length and quality requirements usually determine which plate is selected. For example, little is gained by selecting an expensive plate rated at one million impressions for a short-run house specializing in fast turnaround. Approximate printing life is as follows:

Plate Used	Maximum Run Length
Paper, plastic, or combination	100–10,000
Wipe-on	500–75,000
Presensitized—diazo (negative-working)	10,000–75,000
Presensitized—photopolymer (negative-working)	10,000–1,000,000
Presensitized—diazo or photopolymer (positive-working)	10,000–1,000,000
Multimetal (positive-working or negative-working)	1 million and over

Common plate problems on press include: plate sensitivity, scum, image wear, and image blinding. The description "blind" is applied when the image has been covered up with gum or other water-receptive chemicals. It is important, however, to distinguish between a blind plate and a worn-out plate. If a plate fails to transfer ink but the image is clearly seen, the plate is blind. If the image area is worn or is missing, the plate is worn out.

The major causes of plate problems on press are abrasion of the plate on the press, improper use or application of the

chemicals, faulty ink, faulty paper, improper plate processing, and faulty plate manufacturing.

Problem 1.   **Plate refuses to roll up properly.**

Cause A: Improperly applied finisher.

Remedy:
Wet-wash and rub up the plate on the press until the water
is rejected from the image area. Rinse the plate and use
asphaltum gum etch (A.G.E.) again, applying a very thin
layer.

NOTE: Check with the supplier to be sure you are using the
proper finisher. If the problem occurs in a plate processor,
contact the manufacturer to be sure the equipment is working properly and the correct chemicals are being used.

Cause B: Gum drying in streaks over part or all of the work and
desensitizing it.

Remedy:
Wet-wash the plate thoroughly with hot water, and roll it up
with ink. If this remedy does not help, try an abrasive plate
cleaner or get a new plate. Be sure that the gum or plate finisher is buffed dry with a clean, dry cheesecloth.

Cause C: Unsuitable additive developer used with wipe-on plates.

Remedy:
Relacquer the image using only chemicals and procedures
recommended by the plate manufacturer. Use warm water to
wash up the plate, or apply an A.G.E.

Cause D: Plate has been held too long (at an especially high temperature or humidity) before going to press.

Remedy:
Wet-wash the plate with hot water.

Problem 2.   **Nonimage areas become greasy or scummy.** The ink
adheres to the nonimage area and cannot be removed with a
moistened wipe or sponge.

Cause A: Dirty or worn dampener covers.

Remedy:
Clean or re-cover the dampening rollers. Replace the plate, or clean off the scum with a plate cleaner recommended by the plate manufacturer. (Alkaline cleaners must not be used on unbaked positive-working plates.) Apply a new desensitizing gum or plate finisher.

Cause B: Halftones run with too much ink. The ink squashes on the dots and spreads over the open areas, eventually sensitizing them.

Remedy 1:
Run the ink as stiff and spare as possible.

Remedy 2:
Replace the ink with a more highly pigmented ink.

Cause C: Slurring of halftones. This condition causes open areas in halftones to fill in and the back edges of solids to lose sharpness. It usually results from improper packing, excessive pressure, or excessive ink, especially when printing on coated stocks.

Remedy 1:
Reduce ink feed, and reduce plate-to-blanket and back-cylinder pressures to a minimum.

Remedy 2:
Be sure that the plate and blanket are properly packed so that the surface speed of the two cylinders is the same.

Cause D: Improperly set grippers or dirty gripper pads.

Remedy:
Reset grippers and clean gripper pads on a regular basis.

Cause E: Pit corrosion, sometimes called "ink-dot scum" or "measles." Most aluminum plates are anodized as they are manufactured, which is one reason that they perform as well as they do. Pit corrosion occurs when a wet plate dries too slowly, a plate is stored in a damp area before processing or while being held for a rerun, or the press is stopped during a run with the dampening rollers opposite a moist plate area slowing the drying of this area. On aluminum plates, pit corrosion is a multitude of fine, sharp dots with white centers. This scum usually appears in horizontal streaks.

Remedy:
The best remedy is prevention or care in handling the plates. Always store them in a dry place. During platemaking, dry them with a fan or dry cheesecloth. After shutting down a press, allow it to idle until the plates are dry. If the scum is very light, it may be possible to remove it by etching the plate. If the scum is heavy, the plate should be remade.

Cause F: Plate improperly desensitized when made.

Remedy 1:
Have the plate remade.

Remedy 2:
Reetch and gum the plate on the press, but first, be sure image areas are well protected with ink. Dry the etch thoroughly before washing it off. If this procedure does not remove the scum, try wet-washing the plate and rolling the image up with ink before etching and gumming it.

Cause G: Ink is too soft or greasy.

Remedy:
Stiffen the ink with no. 8 varnish or body gum. If this procedure does not help, try a stiffer ink.

Cause H: Abrasive particles in the ink.

Remedy:
Have the ink reground, or replace it with a better ink.

Cause I: Abrasive particles picked up from the paper surface by the offset blanket.

Remedy 1:
Change to a better stock.

Remedy 2:
Minimize the plate-to-blanket and back-cylinder pressures.

Remedy 3:
Increase water feed.

Remedy 4:
Add a recommended non-piling additive to the dampening solution.

Cause J: Secondary scumming in multicolor printing. This condition can happen on any unit of a multicolor press except the first. Printed ink from one unit is picked up by the offset blanket of the subsequent unit so that the ink contacts the nonimage areas of the plate. If the ink sensitizes these areas, it deposits a scum of that color on the preceding color areas, changing their values.

Remedy 1:
If poor plate desensitization is suspected, reetch and gum up the scumming plate. (See "Cause F" above.)

Remedy 2:
Increase the acid and gum in the dampening solution on the effected plate.

Remedy 3:
Run the ink sparer on the preceding unit. If necessary, use a stronger ink.

Remedy 4:
Move the ink that is backtrapping to the last unit.

Cause K: Plate exposed to light (fogged) before processing.

Remedy 1:
Replace the plate. Be sure plates are not carelessly exposed before processing.

Remedy 2:
When making multiple burns, be sure that light is not exposing the plate through the masking sheets or opaque areas of the film.

Problem 3. **Tinting.** The ink appears in the nonimage area, but it does not adhere to the plate. The ink is easily removed with a moistened thumb or a wet sponge.

Cause A: Ink form rollers set too tightly against the oscillator.

                         Remedy:
                         Readjust rollers to press manufacturer's specifications.

Cause B: Fountain water extracts an emulsifying or sensitizing agent from the paper coating.

                         Remedy:
                         Stiffen the ink with no. 8 varnish or body gum or try a stiffer ink. Avoid using a wetting agent in the dampening solution. If tinting continues, get another paper.

Cause C: Contamination. Any blanket or press wash in the dampening solution can cause tinting. Some press washes can also contaminate the ink.

                         Remedy 1:
                         Be careful when washing up the press. Do not allow washup solvents to mix with the dampening solution.

                         Remedy 2:
                         Avoid using proprietary plate cleaners or other chemicals on the fly since they can contaminate the dampening solution.

                         Remedy 3:
                         Dump the dampening solution, clean the system, and refill it with fresh dampening solution.

                         Remedy 4:
                         Rinse the rollers and blanket with water after cleaning to remove contaminants.

Cause D: Nonimage areas of the plate not well desensitized because of incomplete removal of residual coating. To check for it, wash all tint off the plate, polish part of a blank area with a scotch stone or snakeslip, and give the entire plate a light etch. If, on resuming the run, the polished area remains clean while the surrounding area tints, the cause is residual coating. If all areas continue tinting, the cause is the paper or a breakdown of the ink.

                         Remedy 1:
                         Replace the plate.

Remedy 2:
If the test (Cause C) indicates the presence of residual coating, add more fountain etch; do not reduce the pH of the dampening solution below 4.5 because the ink may not dry.

Cause E: Ink emulsifies in dampening solution. If, in single-color presswork, changing the paper does not stop tinting, the problem is caused by the ink or the plate. In multicolor presswork, if all the inks are tinting, the cause is most likely the paper or dampening solution (see Causes B and C). If one or two inks are tinting while the others are printing clean, an ink problem is indicated.

Remedy 1:
Stiffen the offending inks, or replace them with more water-resistant inks.

Remedy 2:
Change the dampening solution. Be sure that it is mixed properly and not contaminated. Excessive acid in the dampening solution can cause tinting when running too much water.

Remedy 3:
Ensure that the washup solvents do not contaminate the ink.

NOTE: Inks designed for large, high-speed presses often break down and tint on small presses run at lower speeds.

Problem 4.   **Plate fails to print full-strength color.**

Cause A: Image lacks affinity for ink.

Remedy 1:
Wet-wash the plate with hot water. An acidic plate cleaner may be needed to remove gum from the plate image.

Remedy 2:
Treat the plate with A.G.E. or a compatible wipe-on plate developer.

Cause B: Short or water-logged ink piles on the rollers, plate, and blanket.

Remedy 1:
Replace the ink.

Remedy 2:
Reduce dampening solution to a minimum; add alcohol or an alcohol substitute.

Remedy 3:
Lengthen the ink by adding long or water-resistant varnish.

Cause C: Plate starting to go blind.

Remedy:
See remedies for the following problem.

Problem 5.   **Plate blinding** or the image will not transfer ink. The image is clearly seen but fails to transfer ink.

Cause A: Too much gum in the dampening solution.

Remedy:
Drain the water fountain, and fill it with plain tap water. Lift the form rollers. With dampeners on the plate, run waste sheets until ink on the plate is exhausted; then, drop the ink form rollers, and proceed to print. This treatment removes gum sticking to the image areas. Replace the dampening solution with one that is properly prepared.

Cause B: Too much acid in the fountain water. This condition may be indicated by roller stripping or by plate scumming before the plate loses the image.

Remedy:
Drain the fountain, and replace the solution with one mixed according to the manufacturer's specifications.

Cause C: Buildup of calcium or magnesium salts or detergent on the image areas of the plate.

Remedy:
Wash the plate carefully with an acidic plate cleaner or a solution of alcohol, vinegar, and water. Rub up the image with ink, A.G.E., or a compatible wipe-on developer to be sure that the image is ink receptive.

Cause D: Plate-to-blanket pressure is too great. This condition may be due to a swollen, embossed, or overpacked blanket.

Remedy:
Correct the plate-to-blanket pressure. If blanket is badly embossed, replace it.

Cause E: Image lacquer not resistant to blinding.

Remedy:
Try remedy for Cause A, this problem, or go over the plate with A.G.E. or a compatible wipe-on developer.

Problem 6.   **Image loss.** The image disappears or "walks off" of the plate.

Cause A: Plate is worn out.

Remedy 1:
Check plate-to-blanket squeeze and form roller settings to be sure they are not wearing the plate.

Remedy 2:
Replace the plate with a better plate.

Remedy 3:
Check all solvents and cleaners used around the plate to be sure that they do not damage the image.

Cause B: Abrasive paper or ink.

Remedy:
Replace the plate. Consult suppliers to be sure paper and ink are not abrasive. Replace the paper and/or ink if necessary.

Problem 7.   **Bimetal plate goes blind.**

Cause: Desensitized copper image on a stainless steel-copper or aluminum-copper bimetal plate. This condition is caused by a buildup of water-receptive contaminants.

Remedy:
Treat the plate with a cleaner or image sensitizer according to the manufacturer's instructions.

Problem 8.   **Halftones print grainy or sandy.**

Cause A: Coarse or uneven plate or blanket surface.

Remedy 1:
Remake the plate using a finer-grain plate.

Remedy 2:
Use a smoother blanket.

Remedy 3:
Increase the plate-to-blanket squeeze.

Cause B: Too much fountain water. Water emulsifies in the ink and shortens or waterlogs it. Droplets of this emulsified water tend to wet the paper and prevent uniform inking.

Remedy:
Reduce the dampening moisture. If the plate tends to scum, it was probably not desensitized properly.

Cause C: Ink is too long.

Remedy:
Change the ink.

Cause D: Blanket or plate piling.

Remedy:
Clean the plates and blankets.

6　Offset Blanket Problems

Most offset blankets consist of four plies of long-fiber cotton fabric calendered together with a special rubber cement and then coated with a rubber compound on one side. The thickness of this rubber skim-coat varies from 0.012 to 0.020 in. (0.30 to 0.50 mm), but the overall thickness is about 0.060 in. (1.50 mm) on different blankets. Blankets must have uniform thickness. For quality work, the thickness variation must be no more than 0.0005 in. (±0.01 mm). There are also two-, three-, and five-ply offset blankets for special purposes.

On sheetfed presses that were sold in North America, it is standard to use one thickness of a four-ply blanket plus enough packing sheets to raise its surface to the proper level in relation to the cylinder bearers. This level is determined by the press manufacturer's specifications and the image length requirement. Some deviation from the specifications is needed to maintain register when paper stretches between printings in multicolor work, but if the excess packing is greater than around 0.005 in., the resulting slur and dot gain becomes unacceptable.

Some European sheetfed presses use two layers of offset blanket. These give a greater cushion effect in the impression and offer a greater degree of cylinder impression.

Compressible blankets incorporate air in the formulation so that they compress upon contacting the plate instead of bulging on either side of contact as conventional blankets do. Rubber can be displaced but cannot be compressed; therefore, conventional blankets are not compressible. The construction of compressible blankets makes them more resistant to battering and smashing. Although compressible blankets are more forgiving than conventional blankets, excessive squeeze or packing results in more dot gain.

An offset blanket is wrapped around its cylinder and held under sufficient tension to prevent its slipping on the cylinder under the rolling pressure of the printing impression. This tension varies considerably since it is applied manually, but the proper tension varies from 30 to 50 ft.-lb. depending on the blanket and the press.

Using a torque wrench to apply correct and uniform tension is important, especially on multicolor presses. Some presses require a specially modified torque wrench.

When a new blanket is first installed, this tension plus the rolling-out effect of the impression may cause some stretching and make it necessary to tighten the blanket at intervals to take up the slack.

The combined tension and rolling impression reduces the thickness of a new blanket during the first few thousand impressions. If the blanket thickness is measured with an accurate bench micrometer and the calculated thickness of packing is added to give 0.004 in. (0.10 mm) of impression, it may be found that after a few hundred sheets the impression is no longer good. Checking with a packing gauge may show that the blanket has subsided 0.002 in. (0.05 mm) or more and needs additional packing to receive a good impression from the plate.

The skim-coat, or printing surface of blankets, was originally made from natural rubber. Now, it is usually synthetic rubber, which is less oil-absorbent and therefore less susceptible to swelling, embossing, and developing tackiness and glaze. Blanket tackiness has almost ceased to be a problem. Poor release is usually a chemical problem or may be caused by the surface of the blanket.

Glazing occurs when gum, drying oils, and metallic driers are absorbed during printing. These promote surface oxidation, which hardens the rubber and reduces its elasticity and ink receptivity. Strong solvents can also remove plasticizer from the rubber and harden the blanket surface. A glazed blanket fails to transfer ink properly. Removing the glaze by scrubbing with an abrasive pad and solvent restores its printing quality. The blanket surface should have a soft, velvety feel when it is in good condition. A good blanket wash eliminates many blanket problems. If the solvent is too strong, it swells the blanket. If the solvent is too weak, it will not remove the ink or clean the blanket thoroughly. Lithographic chemical suppliers sell specially formulated blanket washes that will remove ink effectively without swelling the blanket or ink rollers.

The following are the principal offset blanket problems.

Problem 1.	**Printed impression gradually loses sharpness or solidity.**
Cause A:	Blanket takes a compression set. Impression is lost because the blanket becomes thinner under the rolling pressure.

Remedy:
Use the packing gauge to check the height of the blanket in relation to the bearer. If it has decreased, add a packing paper of the required thickness. If it has not changed, the problem may be due to deterioration of the plate.

Cause B: Increased impression caused by an embossed or swollen blanket. This condition may be due to a blanket with insufficient resistance to solvent or oil, or continued use of an "aggressive" blanket wash.

Remedy 1:
Check the height of the blanket surface with the packing gauge. If it has increased, remove the indicated thickness of packing. If this does not correct the impression, check the plate image for wear and loss of ink affinity (see Chapter 5).

Remedy 2:
Obtain a better blanket wash.

Cause C: Use of heatset or quickset inks with blankets designed for conventional inks. This can cause excessive pressure embossing the image areas.

Remedy:
Change to a blanket designed for heatset and quickset inks.

Cause D: Loss of ink receptivity because the blanket's surface has become glazed and hard. This can result from oxidation of absorbed drying oils, driers, or gum arabic accumulation.

Remedy:
Wash the blanket with solvent and water; then, scrub it with an abrasive pad and solvent until the glaze is removed.

NOTE: The blanket must be thoroughly cleaned and freed of deposits by using a quality blanket wash. Such washing is a relatively simple way to avoid many blanket problems.

Problem 2: **Ghost image from a previous job.**

Cause: Blanket embossing resulting from ink-vehicle absorption during printing of the previous job.

Remedy 1:
Install a new blanket.

NOTE: Clean the old blanket thoroughly with a rubber rejuvenator and hang it in a dark area to rest. This procedure allows absorbed oil to diffuse through the rubber, possibly reducing the embossing.

Remedy 2:
Consult the inkmaker about solvent content of the ink.

Problem 3. **Paper sticks to nonprinting areas of the blanket.**

Cause: Blanket tackiness resulting from use of strong solvent washes or oxidation of rubber and absorbed drying oils. This is caused by manganese and/or cobalt driers. It is uncommon with modern synthetic rubber blankets.

Remedy 1:
Use a quick-release blanket.

Remedy 2:
Treat the blanket with a blanket lacquer or hardener to relieve the tackiness; however, this relief is only temporary. The blanket should be removed, washed thoroughly, and rested until its tackiness has disappeared. It should then be scrubbed with solvent until its surface glaze is removed.

Problem 4.   **Uneven impression.**

Cause A: Nonuniform blanket thickness. (See Chapter 2, Problem 3.)

                       Remedy:
                       Replace the blanket. Buy quality blankets and check to make
                       sure they are in good condition when they are received.

Cause B: One or more warped cylinders. (See Chapter 2, Problem 3.)

Cause C: Improper cylinder alignment or bearer preload.

                       Remedy:
                       Check the cylinders.

Problem 5.   **Blanket is cut, smashed, or indented.**

Cause: Foreign objects, paper wads, or folded sheets, especially
                       heavy papers and paper board, pass through the press.

                       Remedy 1:
                       If the blanket's surface is cut, replace it. Quality printing
                       cannot be achieved with poor materials.

                       Remedy 2:
                       If the blanket's surface is not cut but is smashed or indented,
                       wash the low area thoroughly with blanket wash to swell it
                       as much as possible. Next, put paper patches under the
                       depressed areas to bring them up to normal height.

Problem 6.   **Horizontal streaks in the printing.**

Cause: Loose or overpacked blanket.

                       Remedy:
                       Tighten the blanket. Use the packing gauge to check the
                       plate-to-blanket pressure; remove any excess packing.

Problem 7.   **Slur.**

Cause A: A loose blanket.

                       Remedy:
                       Tighten the blanket evenly across the width of the press.

Cause B: Blanket bars improperly mounted or adhered to the blanket.

Remedy 1:
Remount the blanket bars properly on the blanket.

Remedy 2:
Install a new blanket.

Cause C: Improper packing under the blanket.

Remedy:
Use quality packing paper. Use a maximum of two sheets.

Problem 8.   **Misregister.**

Cause A: A loose blanket.

Remedy:
Tighten the blanket.

Cause B: Tacky and/or glazed blanket surfaces resulting in uneven separation forces between paper and blanket.

Remedy:
Recondition or replace the blanket.

7 Paper Problems

There are many varieties, grades, and finishes of paper and paperboard. All are composed mainly of cellulose fiber. They have other properties in common, such as grain direction and hygroscopic (i.e., interaction with moisture) properties, but they vary tremendously depending on the cellulose fiber used, the fiber preparation, and the surface and finish given the paper in manufacture.

For satisfactory performance on the press, sheet papers must meet the following basic requirements:

Flatness. The sheets must be flat enough to feed properly and to pass through the impression nip under pressure (squeeze) without wrinkling or distorting.

Proper relative humidity. When skids or feeder piles are exposed to the pressroom atmosphere, the paper must have a relative humidity (RH) close to that in the pressroom (i.e., between 8% RH drier and 8% RH moister), especially when the job calls for two or more printings. Greater RH differences result in wavy or tight edges that cause distortion, misregister, wrinkles, and feeding problems.

Rotronic Hygroscope
GT used to test the
moisture balance of
paper
*Courtesy of
Kaymont Instrument
Corp.*

Because the papermaker must make all paper to one specification and because the printer cannot effectively control this RH, the pressroom RH must be controlled. For paper to be run through the press only once, a RH of 40% to 55% is usually satisfactory. If the sheet is to be run more than once, closer control is required.

Freedom from lint and dust. Loose fibers and dust particles quickly destroy print quality. Furthermore, runnability is impaired if the press operator must frequently stop to clean plates and blankets.

Adequate moisture resistance. The press moisture should not soften surface sizing or coating adhesive enough to permit transfer of surface fibers, mineral filler, or coating pigment to the offset blanket.

Adequate pick resistance. Sufficient surface strength will prevent picking without excessive reduction of ink tack.

Freedom from active chemicals. Paper must contain no chemical that blinds or sensitizes printing plates or causes scumming, tinting, or ink emulsification.

Good ink-drying qualities. The paper should not contribute to setoff, chalking, or other drying problems.

Accurate trimming. Sheets should be trimmed so that edges are straight and corners are square. A convex or concave gripper edge can cause misregister, especially in printing thin, flexible papers. Subsequently, the press operator may have managed to run these sheets only to find that they cannot be handled in the bindery.

In addition to these basic requirements, there are certain qualities required for special work.

Sheet papers for multicolor work should usually be grain long. Dimensional changes, which are much greater across than with the grain, can then be compensated for by changes in plate and blanket packing to maintain fit.

Dimensional stability or resistance to mechanical stretch is important in multicolor work. Part of this stretch is purely

Sheet decurler
Courtesy of
Baldwin-Gegenheimer

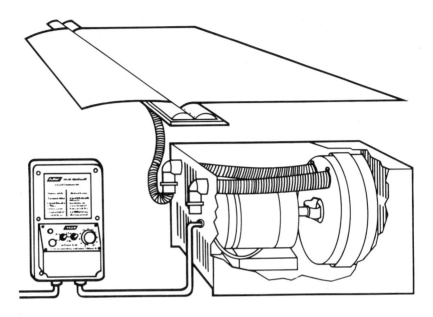

elastic, and the sheets return to their original size. But if there is any permanent stretch, it will vary from sheet to sheet and make register of subsequent colors impossible. Embossed, pebbled, and lightweight papers have poor dimensional stability.

After being printed, some thin papers curl toward the printed side. The paper first curls away from the printed side and then reverses. This curling is caused by the slight moistening that papers get through contact with the offset blanket. It can render labels, wrappers, and other printed articles unusable. Paper can be tested for curling tendency and rejected if it is excessive.

Common paper problems, their causes and remedies, are listed below. When these problems occur, the printer should consult with the paper supplier.

Problem 1.   **Wrinkles or creases.**

Cause A: Front guides, insertion devices, or cylinder grippers not functioning properly. Wheels are set too tight on the register table.

Remedy:

Cause A is press related. (See Chapter 1, "Sheet Feeding and Delivery Problems.")

Cause B: Wavy-edged paper. (See Chapter 1, Problem 9.) Wavy-edged paper is most often caused by unwrapping cold paper. It is sometimes caused by high humidity in the pressroom.

Remedy 1:
Replace wavy paper with more suitable stock.

Remedy 2:
Do not open or unwrap the paper until it has come to room temperature. In the winter, it may take three or four days for the paper to reach room temperature. A steel-jacketed thermometer is useful for measuring the temperature of the paper.

Remedy 3:
Remove the moisture from the air with dehumidifiers. Install an air-conditioning system if the wavy-edged paper causes enough trouble to warrant the cost.

Wavy-edged paper

Remedy 4:
Apply heat to the sides of the feeder pile to warm the edges of the sheets and drive out some of the moisture. Place strip heaters or infrared lamps along the sides of the feeder pile

near the top, or place the load in a hot, dry area for an hour or more before printing. This remedy may get the paper through the press, but it will not produce close register.

Remedy 5:
If the press has a three-point guide system, use a bustle wheel to put a slight kink or wave in the gripper edge of the sheets. This kink or wave pulls the front corners together slightly, relieving the lateral compression on the back half of the sheets.

Remedy 6:
Cut out sections of packing under the side edges of the blanket where there is no printing. This remedy relieves the pressure on the wavy edges that cause "fanning in."

Cause C: Tight-edged or baggy paper, resulting in a wrinkle that starts between the gripper edge and center of the sheets and disappears before reaching their back edge. Paper becomes tight-edged if it is left unwrapped in a dry atmosphere. Tight-edged paper is, in general, more troublesome than wavy-edged paper.

Remedy 1:
Replace the tight-edged paper with a more suitable stock.

Remedy 2:
Cut out sections of packing under the side edges of the blanket where there is no printing. This remedy relieves the pressure on the tight edges that causes "fanning out."

Remedy 3:
Humidify the pressroom. This may take several days to fix tight-edged paper, but it will prevent a recurrence of this condition. Paper becomes tight-edged when the pressroom is too dry. This condition usually occurs in the winter in temperate climates and in the summer in hot, dry climates. Humidifiers are inexpensive to buy and operate and are strongly recommended to prevent this problem. If paper develops tight edges after being printed, creases, wrinkles, misregister, poor trapping, or slurring may prevent backing up the job. The only way to finish the job satisfactorily is to humidify the pressroom until the tight edges are eliminated.

Remedy 4:
Wrap printed lifts in a polyethylene wrapper as soon as they are removed from the press. Like Remedy 3, this will not eliminate a tight-edged paper problem, but it will help prevent it in the future.

Problem 2.   **Poor fit at tail edge.** Two or more printings fail to fit or register. The colors fit along gripper edge, but fail to fit at the back corners. If two images are the same size but are not properly located, the problem is called **misregister.** If the images are different sizes, the problem is poor fit. Misregister is usually not a paper problem; poor fit is often a paper problem.

Cause A: Side edges of sheets pick up moisture between printings and become longer. As a result, the second printing is longer across the back edge than the first printing.

Remedy 1:
Use flat sheets for the first printing. These sheets should print the same length as the plate image along their back edges. Between printings, the piles should be covered with moisture-vapor-proof covers to prevent pickup or loss of moisture.

Remedy 2:
Reduce the amount of water fed to the sheet. Adding alcohol or an alcohol substitute to the water fountain is helpful.

Remedy 3:
Reduce excess impression or back-cylinder squeeze that aggravates rollout or stretch.

Remedy 4:
Expect this problem with embossed or pebbled papers. Run these sheets through the press first without printing to reduce stretch.

Remedy 5:
See Problem 1, Cause B, and pp. 81, 84 for remedies for back-edge wrinkles caused by wavy-edged paper.

Cause B: Side edges of sheets lose moisture between printings and become shorter than they were originally. As a result, the second printing is shorter than the first printing across the back edge.

Remedy 1:
See Cause A, Remedy 1, this problem.

Remedy 2:
See Problem 1, Cause C, for remedies.

Cause C: Plate and blanket not properly packed for the desired print length.

Remedy 1:
If the second printing is longer than the first, transfer packing sheets from the blanket to the plate cylinder until the print is shortened sufficiently to register.

Remedy 2:
If the second printing is shorter than the first, transfer packing sheets from the plate to the blanket cylinder until the print is lengthened sufficiently to register.

NOTE 1: The change in image length caused by transfer of a packing sheet can be calculated approximately by the following formula:

$$L = p(0.0125)X$$

where L is the change in image length in inches, p is the thickness of the packing sheet in mils (0.001 in.), and X is the fraction of cylinder circumference occupied by the plate image. Example: If the thickness of the packing sheet (p) is 1 mil and the fraction (X) of the cylinder occupied by the plate image is 0.66, the change (increase or decrease) in image length (L) in inches is 0.008 in. ($1 \times 0.0125 \times 0.66$).

NOTE 2: When a job requires multiple printings, it is always good practice to run the first color short; in other words, with the plate packed somewhat above bearer height. This compensates for paper stretch due to moisture pickup and the squeeze impression "ironing-out" effect. Succeeding impressions are then lengthened.

Problem 3. **Poor fit at gripper edge.**

Cause A: Sheets have expanded across the grain between printings because of moisture pickup in the first printing. As a result, the second printing falls inside the first printing on the off-guide side. Expansion is limited with grain-long paper but serious if the paper is grain-short.

Remedy 1:
Remake the plate. Use the first printing as a key, and step the subjects out to fit it.

Remedy 2:
Dupe the film. Cut and restrip the pieces, and remake the plate using the first print as a guide to achieve image fit.

Cause B: Side guide is not functioning properly. The second printing is the same width as first printing, but side register varies. Front guides, sheet-forwarding mechanism, or grippers functioning improperly. The second printing is the same length as the first printing, but the register varies from sheet to sheet.

Remedy:
See Chapter 1, "Sheet Feeding and Delivery Problems."

Problem 4.   **Variable fit.** The second printing fits at the gripper edge but shows variable sheet-to-sheet fit along the back edge that cannot be corrected by adjustments in the plate and blanket packing.

Cause A: Some sheets stretch more than others from front to back in one or both of the printings. This condition sometimes happens with lightweight papers that have been multiple sheeted at the mill. The sheets from some rolls stretch more than others.

Remedy:
Catch any variable mechanical stretch at the start of the first printing. Register marks, front and back, bleeding to the side edges of the sheet will show variable stretch in delivered sheets or a second printing of the same sheet.

The problem is caused by paper lacking stretch resistance. This is most common in lightweight paper grades. It is also caused by excessive back-cylinder pressure. If the variable stretch problem is not eliminated by reducing the back-cylinder pressure to the amount of pressure normally required for a good print, the paper should be set aside because it is unsuitable for multicolor printing.

Cause B: Cockled or embossed papers that are not truly flat. When printed, the squeeze impression rolls them flat, momentarily producing dimensional changes and distortions that vary from sheet to sheet. These papers may recover all or part of their original dimensions after printing. Embossing also weakens paper, making it more susceptible to permanent mechanical stretch.

Remedy:
Minimize stretch by printing with minimal pressure. However, a pressure that permits good register is often not enough to produce a good impression. For this reason, it is not advisable to attempt close register work on cockled or embossed papers, especially on large sheets or lightweight papers.

Cause C: Large solids on some areas of the sheets. The high gripper tension required to separate such solid areas from the offset blanket stretches the sheets permanently in these areas while the other areas remain unstretched. Sometimes the stretched solid areas appear to be embossed. Often this stretch varies from sheet to sheet, making it impossible to fit succeeding colors.

Paper adhering to the blanket in solid areas, causing stretch, embossing, and curl

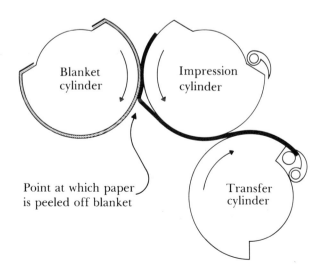

Blanket cylinder

Impression cylinder

Point at which paper is peeled off blanket

Transfer cylinder

Remedy 1:
Reduce the ink's tack as much as possible without affecting print quality.

Remedy 2:
Change to a stronger or heavier paper.

Remedy 3:
Use a quick-release blanket.

Problem 5.   **Poor fit on multicolor press.** Poor fit occurs on a single pass through a multicolor press. Colors fit along the gripper edge, but fail to fit at the back corners. This problem occurs when two or more colors are involved. The interval between impressions on a multicolor press is normally about 1 sec.— too short of a time for the sheets to lose their original flatness or to become wavy or tight-edged.

Cause A: Wavy-edged paper results in colors printing longer across the back edge of the sheets than the plate image. This condition, which is easily determined with a precision calibrated metal rule, does not cause misregister if each sheet distorts in exactly the same way in the successive printing units. The distortion, however, varies slightly from unit to unit, causing back-edge misregister that varies from sheet to sheet.

Remedy 1:
Use flat paper to prevent sheet distortion. Misregister worsens as distortion increases.

Remedy 2:
See Problem 1, Cause B, for remedies for back-edge wrinkles caused by wavy-edged paper.

Cause B: Tight-edged paper results in colors printing shorter across the back edges of the sheets than the plate image. If the tight-edge condition is very bad, it can cause misregister in the body of the sheets, and even wrinkling or creasing.

Remedy 1:
Start with flat paper to eliminate distortion and misregister.

Remedy 2:
See Problem 1, Cause C, for remedies.

Problem 6.   **Slur.** Slur can be caused by too much back-cylinder pressure when printing coated stock, too much plate-to-blanket pressure when running smooth, ungrained plates, or too much ink. It can also be caused by the sheets rippling as they enter the impression nip, which allows some areas to contact the blanket prematurely. See Chapter 2, Problem 4.

Problem 7.   **Doubling of halftones on a multicolor press.**
See Chapter 2, "Printing Unit Problems."

Problem 8.   **White spots or grainy halftones** (lint and fibers on blanket).

Cause A: The loosely bonded surface fibers (e.g., lint, fuzz, fluff, and whiskers) of uncoated paper are lifted by inks, even when a single color is being printed. Once attached to the blanket or plate, they absorb moisture and fail to transfer ink.

Remedy 1:
Use a sheet cleaner to remove loose paper debris.

A solid printed on linty paper, enlarged

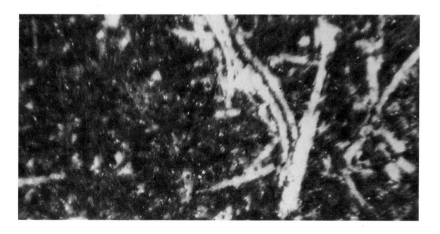

Remedy 2:
Replace the paper.

Remedy 3:
Run the paper through the press using a clean, dry blanket to remove loose debris.

Remedy 4:
Increase ink feed.

Remedy 5:
Increase the water feed.

Remedy 6:
Reduce the ink's tack as much as possible without affecting print quality. If the paper still lints, it should be replaced.

Remedy 7:
Add a nonpiling additive to the dampening solution.

Remedy 8:
Replace the dampening solution.

Remedy 9:
Apply sizing to the paper on a unit prior to printing.

Cause B: Surface fibers of surface-sized paper are not well bonded but are held down by the starch surface size. Such paper usually causes no problem on a single-color press. However, on a multicolor press, moisture from the first unit softens the surface size so that fibers are lifted by the second-down ink or a later ink.

Remedy 1:
Minimize plate dampening. Add alcohol or a substitute to the dampening water to reduce the amount of water required.

Remedy 2:
Apply a press size to the paper prior to printing.

Cause C: Cotton fibers from molleton or other fabric dampening roller covers. These are easy to distinguish from paper fibers. There are less cotton fibers than paper fibers, and the average length of a cotton fiber is more than ⅛ in. (3 mm).

Remedy 1:
Wash the molleton covers before using them.

Remedy 2:
Put new covers on the dampeners.

Remedy 3:
Change to parchment paper dampener covers, or retrofit the press with one of the newer plate dampening systems.

Remedy 4:
Reverse one dampener and/or the ductor end for end.

Problem 9.   **Rough solids.**

Cause A: Surface fibers on uncoated paper not well bonded and raised, but not actually picked up by the pull of the ink.

Remedy 1:
Replace the paper.

Remedy 2:
Increase ink feed.

Remedy 3:
Reduce the ink tack.

Remedy 4:
Use a quick-release blanket.

Cause B: Excess spray powder.

Remedy 1:
Adjust spray powder applicator.

Remedy 2:
Select a finer grade of spray powder.

Remedy 3:
Use a coated spray powder to reduce particle clumping.

Problem 10.   **White spots in solids.** Spots repeat on consecutive sheets and increase in number during the pressrun.

Cause A: Loose paper dust on the sheets.

Remedy 1:
Install a vacuum sheet cleaner.

Remedy 2:
Replace the paper.

Remedy 3:
Run dry paper through a press before printing the job.

Remedy 4:
Increase the water feed. Water causes many problems, but it reduces dust and debris accumulation on the blanket.

Remedy 5:
Add a nonpiling additive to the dampening solution.

Remedy 6:
Size the sheet on the first unit or prior to printing.

Cause B:
Flakes of coating or particles larger than single fibers picked from the paper surface. To distinguish them from loose dust particles, look through the printed sheets for the sheet where a flake or particle first appears. If examination with a magnifier shows that the paper surface in the original spot was ruptured, the paper was picked. If not, the spot was caused by a loose dust particle.

Remedy 1:
Obtain a better paper stock.

Remedy 2:
Reduce the ink tack as much as possible without affecting print quality.

Remedy 3:
Increase ink feed. This remedy releases the paper more readily and tends to carry debris away.

Remedy 4:
Use a quick-release blanket.

Problem 11.
Paper picks, splits, or tears. Picking refers to the ink pull rupturing the paper surface areas larger than single fibers. In splitting, larger areas of paper peel off and stick to the blanket; these often develop into V-shaped tears extending to the back edge of the sheets. Delamination occurs when the ink pull causes internal separation without actually rupturing the paper surface. Picking, splitting, and tearing almost always occur in solids, but seldom happen in halftone areas. Since these problems are most likely to occur in solids near the back edge of the sheets, lay out the form with solid areas away from the back edge whenever possible.

Cause A: Paper's internal bond strength is too low or the bond of coating to base stock is too weak to withstand the ink's pull.

Remedy 1:
Reduce the ink tack with a suitable reducer or solvent.

Remedy 2:
Increase ink feed to improve paper release.

Remedy 3:
Reduce press speed.

Remedy 4:
Change to a quick-release blanket.

Remedy 5:
Reduce back-cylinder pressure to a minimum.

Paper picked and torn near back edge of sheet

Remedy 6:
Change to a better paper.

Cause B: Paper with good pick resistance when dry is weakened by successive applications of moisture in multicolor presswork. In this case, the first-down color prints fine, but the second, third, or fourth color picks the paper.

Remedy 1:
Minimize the plate moisture. Using alcohol or an alcohol substitute (a wetting agent) will help.

Remedy 2:
See all remedies under Cause A for this problem.

Problem 12.   **Paper slips in the grippers or pulls out of them.** This problem is press or ink related. The paper is not at fault (see Chapter 1, Problem 10).

Problem 13.   **Sheets curl on delivery and fail to jog properly.** This problem occurs principally in the printing of lightweight papers.

Cause A: Press moisture expands the printed side of the paper, causing the sheets to curl downward. In extreme cases, the sheets roll up like mailing tubes.

Remedy:
Reduce the press moisture to a minimum. Add alcohol or an alcohol substitute (a wetting agent) to the dampening solution to reduce the amount needed. Refrigerate the dampening system.

Cause B: Ink tack distorts the paper as it is peeled from the blanket.

Remedy 1:
Use a quick-release blanket.

Remedy 2:
Minimize the back-cylinder pressure.

Remedy 3:
Decrease ink tack and increase ink feed to improve paper release.

Remedy 4:
Reduce press speed.

Remedy 5:
Avoid layouts having solids near the back edge.

Remedy 6:
Change to a heavier sheet.

Remedy 7:
Install a sheet decurler on the press.

Remedy 8:
Install a static elimination device.

Remedy 9:
If the job requirements allow, run the paper grain short.

Problem 14.   **Reverse curl.** Sheets curl toward the printed side after standing for a time in delivery piles. This curling occurs mostly with lightweight papers that tend to curl downward on delivery. The original curl reverses after the sheets stand in the pile. This problem occurs with two-sided sheets, and it should be discussed with the paper supplier.

Cause A: Press moisture swelling the surface, relaxing its original tensions, and causing the sheet to curl toward the printed side.

Remedy 1:
Keep dampening to a minimum. Use alcohol or a wetting agent.

Remedy 2:
If the job is completed and the curl discovered before the sheets are cut, run the sheets through a single-color press, using a blank plate and applying dampening solution to the back side of the sheets.

Remedy 3:
Refrigerate the dampening system.

Cause B: Paper with excessive curling tendency.

Remedy:
Replace or avoid using such the paper. Paper can be pretested for curling tendency. (See the GATF book *What the Printer Should Know about Paper*.)

Problem 15.   **Paper embosses or "waffles" in solid areas.** Solid areas in the printed sheets are slightly curled and protrude upward, giving an embossed effect. This problem is most common with lightweight papers.

Cause: Simultaneous stretching due to stock weakness and sharp-angle peel-off from the blanket caused by ink tack. The condition strongly resembles tail-end hook.

Remedy:
If the work is done on a multicolor press in a single printing, run the paper grain-short. Be sure that the paper is flat. If the paper is not flat, distortion and misregister will result. If register requirements are very critical, avoid this remedy.

Problem 16.   **Nonimage piling or dusting.** A little piling does not usually affect print quality. If it continues to accumulate, halftones become sandy and highlight dots are lost.

Cause A: Running coated or film-coated paper in which the coating adhesive is water-soluble or lacks wet-rub resistance.

Remedy 1:
Avoid coated papers that have poor wet-rub resistance.

Remedy 2:
Reduce the amount of dampening solution to the minimum required to keep nonimage areas of the plate clean.

Remedy 3:
Refrigerate the dampening solution.

Remedy 4:
Make sure that the blanket is properly packed.

Remedy 5:
Add a nonpiling additive to the dampening solution.

Remedy 6:
Add one part isopropyl alcohol to three parts dampening solution to reduce the solubility of starch coating adhesive.

Cause B: Filler in uncoated papers accumulates on the blanket.

Remedy 1:
Increase water feed to improve blanket release and wash away filler.

Remedy 2:
Add a nonpiling additive to the water fountain.

Cause C: Dusty or "dirty" paper.

Remedy 1:
Increase water feed.

Remedy 2:
Replace the paper.

Remedy 3:
Install a sheet cleaner on the press.

Problem 17.   **Image piling.** The midtones develop a mottled appearance due to dot gain, and the blanket shows a lumpy buildup in halftone areas. This occurs only on the second or later units of multicolor presses—never on the first unit.

Cause: Softened, tacky coating adhesive, ruined by moisture on the first unit, allows ink on the following unit to lift traces of adhesive and coating pigment. These materials mix with the ink, producing a combination that sticks to the blanket and gradually produces a pile of appreciable thickness. Frequent blanket washups with water and ink solvent are needed.

Piling is an immensely complex problem that often appears and disappears for no apparent reason. Increasing or decreasing the amount of dampening will sometimes solve the problem, as will increasing or decreasing the press speed. Adding a nonpiling additive (purchased from a lithographic chemicals supplier) to the dampening solution is often effective. All remedies that reduce the force required to remove the paper from the blanket are helpful.

Remedy 1:
Reduce the amount of dampening.

Remedy 2:
Refrigerate the dampening solution.

Remedy 3:
Add more alcohol or alcohol substitute.

Remedy 4:
Change the press speed.

Blanket piling

Remedy 5:
Use a nonpiling additive in the dampening solution.

Remedy 6:
Decrease the ink tack.

Remedy 7:
Increase the ink feed. (Adding a reducing varnish forces the press operator to feed more ink to maintain color.)

Remedy 8:
Reduce the back-cylinder pressure to a minimum.

Remedy 9:
Change to a quick-release blanket.

Remedy 10:
Change to a more moisture-resistant paper.

Problem 18.   **Tinting.** An overall tint quickly appears on the unprinted areas of coated paper. This tint may appear on the nonimage areas of the plates but can be washed off with a wet sponge. If another paper is substituted, the tint disappears, but quickly returns if the original paper is used again.

Cause: Dampening solution extracts an ink-emulsifying agent from the paper coating.

Remedy 1:
Get a better ink.

Remedy 2:
Stiffen the ink as much as possible with no. 8 varnish or body gum, or try a stiffer ink. Avoid using any wetting agent in the fountain water.

Remedy 3:
Add more alcohol or an alcohol substitute.

Remedy 4:
Refrigerate the dampening solution.

Remedy 5:
If tinting continues, get another paper.

Problem 19.   **Periodic defects.** Sometimes every third, fourth, or fifth printed sheet varies in gloss, color, fit, curl, or some other characteristic.

Cause: In sheeting paper, the papermaker takes several rolls (three, four, or five) and threads them through the sheeter. The papermaker tries to choose rolls that are as much alike as possible. If one roll differs significantly, the properties of prints on paper coming from that roll will differ.

Remedy 1:
Try to minimize the problem by adjusting the ink, the dampening solution, or the press.

Remedy 2:
Set the paper aside for another less critical job.

Remedy 3:
Reject the paper, and have the supplier replace it.

8 Ink Problems

Inks supplied to lithographers vary widely in formulation and properties. The variation is needed because of the wide range of surfaces being printed, the characteristics of different presses, and the various end-use requirements of printed jobs. There are inks for general commercial work that can be adjusted by the lithographer to suit a variety of papers. There are also inks designed especially for label printing, posters, magazine covers, greeting cards, decals, foils, plastics, metal decorating, or other purposes; these inks are usually press-ready and require little or no adjustment by the lithographer. Regardless of the surface to be printed, inks can be varied in transparency, finish, rub-, scuff-, and heat-resistance, lightfastness, chemicals, and solvents.

Consequently, there are thousands of different ink formulations, each formulated for a specific paper or substrate or for a range of substrates, and for a specific set of printing conditions and end-use requirements. There is no ink that is best for all conditions. An ink that is suited for a wide range of papers and end-uses will not be best for any use. The printer must work with the inkmaker to obtain the best inks.

Printing ink is a dispersion of pigment in a fluid vehicle. The pigment provides the color and determines whether the printed ink film will be transparent or opaque. The vehicle gives the ink fluidity so it can be distributed by the press inking rollers and applied evenly to the form. In the printed ink film, the vehicle must change or be changed to a solid in order to bind the pigment to the printed surface.

Inks dry by different methods. Conventional inks contain drying oils that dry by a combination of absorption and chemical action, namely, oxidation and polymerization. Quickset inks contain drying oils and resins, plus solvents that speed up setting by a process of selective absorption. Their final drying is also by oxidation and polymerization. They are most useful on coated papers and boards. Heatset inks that dry by evaporation of a solvent are seldom used on sheetfed presses.

The two major causes of drying problems are using an ink that is improper for the job or using too much water and too much acid (RH too high, pH too low).

All lithographic inks must work with moisture. Dampening water always mixes with the ink to some extent during printing, but the ink must not become waterlogged and pasty or break down and mix with the water. Ink that emulsifies readily gets into the fountain and tints the entire sheet. The inkmaker selects the proper pigments and vehicles and adjusts the ink's body to meet these requirements.

The variables in inkmaking and lithography are almost infinite. Offset press operators face ink problems that require knowledge, experience, and good judgment to solve.

It is recommended that the ink be press-ready in the can, so time-consuming changes are avoided. To get the right ink every time requires close cooperation between printer and inkmaker. Therefore, always consult the inkmaker who is more familiar with the formulation of printing inks and the use of additives to cure problems.

This section gives press operators a ready reference that will help them to avoid ink problems or diagnose them quickly and correctly.

Further information is available in two texts published by GATF: *What the Printer Should Know about Ink* and *Solving Offset Ink Problems*.

Problem 1.   **Ink dries too slowly.** This is usually not discovered until the job has been run. Saving such a job can be much more expensive than preventing the problem.

Cause A: Ink unsuitable for the job.

Remedy 1:
Discuss the job with the inkmaker before running the job. The best cure for a drying problem is prevention. When a drying problem occurs anyway, consult the inkmaker afterward.

Remedy 2:
Avoid altering the ink. When alterations are necessary, consult the inkmaker.

Remedy 3:
Prevent this problem by making a drying test of the ink on the paper to be printed before starting the job.

Remedy 4:
Print over the faulty prints with a varnish that has been demonstrated to dry hard.

Cause B: Too much acid in the dampening water.

Remedy 1:
Keep the dampening solution pH between 4.5 and 5.5.

Remedy 2:
Overprint the wet ink with a transparent size containing drier or with an overprint varnish.

Cause C: Insufficient drier in the ink.

Remedy 1:
Prevent this problem by making a drying test of the ink on the paper to be printed before starting the job.

Remedy 2:
To save the job, use an overprint varnish or overprint the wet ink with a transparent size containing drier, as in Cause B, Remedy 2.

Cause D: Lack of oxygen to dry the ink. This condition can happen when printing large areas of heavy solids.

Remedy:
Wind the sheets several times during the drying period. Keep in mind that "winding" or "airing" the lift may scratch

or mark the sheets if it is done too soon or if it is not done carefully.

Cause E: Temperature of the pressroom or the paper is too low.

Remedy 1:
Maintain the pressroom temperature at 70–75°F (21–25C°). If this remedy is not practical, one of the following should help:

1. Install infrared lamps over the feedboard to warm the paper as it is fed.

2. Install infrared lamps over the delivery pile to warm the sheets as they are delivered.

3. Install an infrared heating unit on the press.

When using any one of these heating methods, remember to shut off the heat the moment printing is interrupted.

Remedy 2:
Allow cold paper to reach the pressroom temperature before starting to print. Keep the paper wrapped so it doesn't develop wavy edges.

Problem 2.   **Hickeys.** Hickeys are caused by dirt or foreign particles on the plate or blanket. They can come from many sources: ink, paper, press, and pressroom. Carelessly handling the ink in the manufacturing process or in the pressroom could result in ink skins or particles of dried ink in the can, which will

A typical ink-skin hickey, enlarged

cause hickeys. A dirty press or one that is poorly maintained is a common cause of hickeys.

Cause A: Dried ink or other dirt on the press.

Remedy 1:
Keep the press clean.

Remedy 2:
Keep rollers in good condition.

Cause B: Dirt in the pressroom.

Remedy 1:
Keep the pressroom clean.

Dirt shield over feeder of sheetfed press

Remedy 2:
Hang a plastic shield over the press.

Remedy 3:
Use hickey-picking rollers on the press.

Hickeys

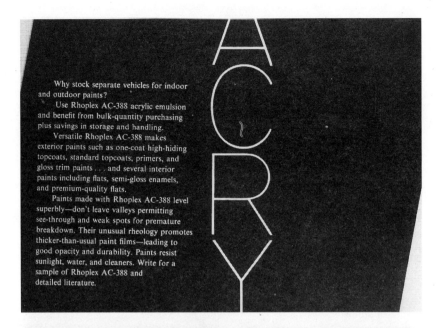

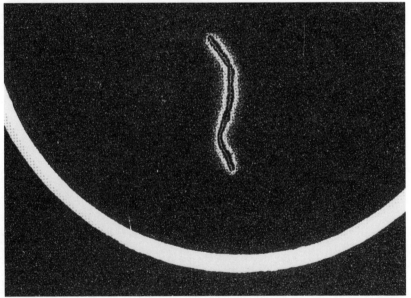

Remedy 4:
Use a hickey picker to remove dirt from the plate or blanket.

Remedy 5:
Run a thicker ink film. This remedy tends to wash hickeys from the plate.

Cause C: Ink skin or dried ink in the can.

Remedy:
Send the ink back to the inkmaker. Be sure that pressroom personnel know how to handle the ink. Ink saved at the end of a run should be stored only under a skin sheet in a tightly covered can.

Cause D: Dirty paper.

Remedy 1:
Use a sheet cleaner to remove dirt from the paper.

Remedy 2:
Send the paper back to the papermaker.

Problem 3.   **Scumming.** Scum is usually visible on the plate and cannot be removed with a water sponge. If light, it can sometimes be corrected by reetching the plate. Ink can cause scumming, but there are many other causes not related to ink.

Cause A: Running too much ink or running an ink that is too soft. The ink squashes and spreads over the nonprinting areas between the dots, gradually sensitizing these areas.

Remedy:
Run the ink on halftones as stiff and spare as possible.

Cause B: Ink improperly formulated. The inkmaker sometimes receives contaminated raw materials that promote scumming when they are used in ink.

Remedy:
Send the ink back to the inkmaker.

Cause C: Too much drier or compound in the ink.

Remedy 1:
Avoid altering the ink in the pressroom. Consult the inkmaker.

Remedy 2:
Use as little drier as possible. If conditions require more than 1 oz. of regular drier per pound (60 g per kilogram) of

ink, use a concentrated drier. Avoid adding compounds if possible.

Cause D: Abrasive particles in the ink. These gradually wear the plate at the margins of its image areas, causing images to thicken.

Remedy:
Have the ink reground or replace it with a better ink.

Cause E: Plate problems. (See Chapter 4.)

Problem 4.   **Setoff.**

Cause A: The ink isn't adjusted to the absorbency of the surface being printed. Ink fails to set before the next sheet contacts it on the delivery pile. This happens if the ink vehicle penetrates the paper too slowly or the paper lacks absorbency.

Remedy 1:
If the problem occurs in printing on coated paper with conventional ink, change to a quickset ink.

Remedy 2:
Apply or increase the amount of spray powder; use the minimum required to prevent setoff, especially if the job requires additional printings or good scuff-resistance.

Remedy 3:
Add 0.5 to 1.0 oz. of boiled linseed oil or no. 0000 varnish per pound (30 to 60 g per kilogram) of ink. A small amount of heatset or quickset solvent will accomplish the same result.

Remedy 4:
Avoid piling sheets high on the delivery. In the case of aluminum foil and plastics, remove the sheets from the delivery in small lifts and rack them for drying.

Remedy 5:
Use an ink with higher tack.

Remedy 6:
Use an infrared panel to speed the setting of ink. If setoff is a continual problem, invest in an IR system.

Remedy 7:
Add a small amount of antisetoff compound to the ink. Use as little antisetoff compound as possible, since an excess will reduce the rub- and scuff-resistance of the ink, increase blanket piling, and prevent trapping and adhesion of inks.

Cause B: Rough handling of skids of freshly printed sheets.

Remedy 1:
Check alignment of the delivery joggers. Realign them if necessary.

Remedy 2:
Avoid lowering delivery skid to the floor too fast.

Remedy 3:
Avoid trucking skids over rough floors. Avoid sudden starts and stops in trucking.

Cause C: Running too much ink increases setting time.

An electronic
Inkometer
*Courtesy of
Thwing-Albert
Instrument Co.*

Remedy:
Run a stronger ink spare. Reduce the water to a minimum.

Cause D: Sheets embossed or waffled in printing. When solids are embossed, succeeding sheets contact the embossed areas before the ink on them has set. The normal air cushion is not effective during jogging.

Remedy 1:
Use an antisetoff spray powder. (See Cause A, Remedy 2.)

Remedy 2:
Increase the penetrating power of the ink. (See Cause A, Remedy 3.)

Remedy 3:
If possible, use paper with less tendency toward embossing. If the work is done in a single printing on a multicolor press, try running the paper grain-short.

Remedy 4:
Install a sheet decurler on the press.

Cause E:
Curly or bumpy paper. Such paper acts similarly to paper embossed in printing. (See Cause D, this problem.)

Remedy:
Use an antisetoff powder. Increase the ink's penetration and setting rate. Run the ink spare.

Cause F:
Printing with gloss inks. Gloss inks have minimum penetration on paper with high ink holdout. Waxes in gloss inks tend to prevent setoff, but seldom work on the highest gloss ink.

Remedy 1:
Use an antisetoff powder, but use as little as possible. Excess powder reduces rub- and scuff-resistance. Do not allow sheets to pile high on the delivery; but remove them and let them dry in small lifts.

Remedy 2:
Evaluate the operation of the spray powder system. Adjust or maintain as necessary.

Problem 5.
Ink picks, splits, or tears the paper. This problem is ink and paper related. The ink is too tacky for the paper under the conditions on press. Since picking, splitting, and blistering problems are also caused by paper weakness, they are discussed in Chapter 7, "Paper Problems."

Cause A: The ink is too tacky for the paper.

Remedy 1:
Reduce the ink's tack with a suitable reducer or solvent.

Remedy 2:
If Remedy 1 reduces print quality too much, change to a more pick-resistant paper.

Remedy 3:
Increase the ink film thickness. A slight increase in ink film thickness is often very effective in reducing picking.

Cause B: Conventional ink drying and increased ink tack on press. This may be caused by too much cobalt drier in the ink.

Remedy 1:
Add no. 00 varnish to the ink to reduce its initial tack.

Remedy 2:
Add a little "slow-dry" or antioxidant compound to the ink. Consult the inkmaker first.

Remedy 3:
Obtain another batch of ink with less drier.

Cause C: Quickset or heatset ink loses solvent and increases in tack during press stops. This condition can be caused by newly covered rubber ink rollers absorbing solvent, or by evaporating solvent, or both.

Remedy 1:
Consult the inkmaker.

Remedy 2:
If the roller composition is new, or if the rollers have been standing dry for any duration, saturate them with an ink solvent before inking up the press.

Remedy 3:
During press stops, spray the ink rollers with a commercial spray to keep the ink from drying.

Remedy 4:
Soften the ink in the fountain to counteract the stiffening caused by solvent evaporation during makeready. Once the run is started and the ink flow established, the regular ink should cause no problem.

Cause D: Quickset ink continues to pick paper after the run has been started.

Remedy 1:
Have the ink reformulated with a less volatile solvent.

Remedy 2:
Add 0.5 oz. of a 0000 varnish per pound of ink (30 g per kg).

Problem 6.   **Mechanical ghosting.**

Cause: A narrow solid ahead or behind a wider solid robs the form roller of the ink needed to print full-strength color in a corresponding area of the wider solid. Lateral distribution does not provide the extra ink needed in narrow sections to prevent ghosting.

Remedy 1:
Whenever possible, have the solids well distributed on the layout.

Remedy 2:
Run a minimum of dampening solution. Use alcohol or an alcohol substitute.

Remedy 3:
Run a thicker ink film. Avoid running colors spare to produce tints. Make the color weaker and run more of it.

Remedy 4:
If possible, use opaque inks rather than transparent inks for solids.

Remedy 5:
Increase the pitch on the oscillator.

Remedy 6:
Install an oscillating form roller in the last position.

Remedy 7:
Reduce the hardness of the form roller, or get new rollers.

Remedy 8:
Cock the image on the plate so that ghosted images do not run straight around the cylinder.

Problem 7.   **Ink chalks on coated paper.** Chalking is the condition in which the ink appears dry but can be rubbed off easily.

Cause A: Excessive vehicle penetration. This condition can be caused by improperly altered or improperly formulated ink or by a paper with high absorbency.

Remedy 1:
Consult the inkmaker. Obtain an ink suited to the paper.

Remedy 2:
Add body gum (no. 8 varnish), gel varnish, gloss varnish, or a binding varnish to decrease the vehicle's penetration rate.

Cause B: Delayed drying. If drying is too slow, too much vehicle is absorbed before gelling takes place, and the pigment is left without sufficient binder.

Remedy 1:
Review the causes of delayed drying of conventional and quickset inks. Any one of these problems could also cause chalking. Apply the indicated remedy.

Remedy 2:
Chalking is not usually evident until hours after the sheets are printed. However, a chalked job can often be saved by overprinting the work with a transparent size or overprint varnish to supply the required binder.

Problem 8.   **Ruboff.** An ink is dry but rubs during folding and binding.

Cause: Weak film caused by nondrying materials in the ink.

Remedy 1:
Avoid the problem by having the inkmaker formulate the right ink for the paper.

Remedy 2:
Avoid using ink additives such as cup grease, petroleum, or mineral oil. Use only additives that are approved by the inkmaker. Keep all additives to a minimum. Nondrying materials plasticize the dried ink film and decrease its rub-resistance. Driers contain some nondrying components. Avoid using excessive drier.

Problem 9.   **Poor coating adhesion and nonuniform coating lay.**

Cause A: Wax or similar materials added to ink to improve rub resistance.

Remedy:
Use wax-free ink if coating is to be applied.

Cause B: Slow-drying ink interferes with the adhesion of the coating to the ink.

Remedy 1:
Use faster-drying inks.

Remedy 2:
Use a drying accelerator in the dampening solution.

Cause C: Alcohol substitutes contain chemicals that do not evaporate like isopropyl alcohol. When these chemical become concentrated in the recirculation system due to water evaporation and are emulsified into the ink, they can interfere with coating adhesion.

Remedy:
Clean the recirculator, and change the dampening solution at least once a week.

Problem 10.   **Nonuniform ink lay and adhesion to plastic.**

Cause A: Too low surface energy.

Remedy:
Use a plastic that is corona-treated with a surface energy of 40–50 dynes.

Cause B: Inks not properly formulated for plastic.

Remedy:
Use high-solid, low-solvent inks.

Cause C: Inks are over-emulsified.

Remedy:
When printing on nonabsorbent substrates, inks must be formulated with a lower water pick-up, and the minimum amount of water should be used.

Problem 11. **Scuffing or marring** of covers, labels, or cartons.

Cause: Ink not scuff-proof on the printed stock.

Remedy 1:
Obtain inks made to be scuff-resistant on the printed stock. Since ink that is scuff-proof on one stock is not necessarily scuff-proof on another, making and testing proofs before printing the job will ensure that suitable inks are used.

Remedy 2:
Replace the paper. Some papers are highly abrasive.

Problem 12. **Scuffing of covers during shipping.**

Cause A: Insecurely wrapped books, which may be loose enough to rub against each other during shipment.

Remedy:
Book covers that are scratched during shipment cannot be repaired. Sometimes it is more economical to remove the scuffed covers and replace them than it is to reprint the entire job. The only solution is to prevent rubbing, scuffing, or abrasion by wrapping and binding the books securely.

Cause B: Varnish not adequate for the job.

Remedy:
Be sure the varnish is properly formulated for the job. Covers scuffed due to inadequate varnish must be discarded.

Cause C: Excess spray powder. Spray powder that prevents offsetting may promote abrasion.

Remedy:
Keep spray powder application at a minimum and wrap books or catalogs securely for shipment.

Problem 13.   **Dry trapping.** Ink fails to trap on a previously printed and dried color because the previously printed ink has crystallized. Actually, a nondrying oil or wax has oozed to the paper's surface, making it nonreceptive to fresh ink.

Cause: Too much grease or wax compound in the dried ink.

Remedy 1:
Discuss ink requirements with the inkmaker, preferably before the job is run.

Remedy 2:
Avoid grease and wax compounds in inks where a second printing is to follow. Keep drier to a minimum, since driers usually contain some nondrying materials.

Remedy 3:
Make succeeding printings as soon as the previous ink is dry enough to permit handling the sheets. The longer an ink is allowed to dry, the more nondrying materials will ooze to its surface and interfere with trapping.

Remedy 4:
Use a paste drier in the first-down colors, if the press operator adds the driers to the inks. The amount of cobalt drier used should be kept to a minimum.

Remedy 5:
Add a trapping compound to ink that fails to trap.

Problem 14.   **Ink crystallization.** An ink traps on a previously printed and dried color but, when dry, it lacks adhesion. It can easily be scratched off with the fingernail.

Cause: First-down ink crystallizes—not enough to prevent trapping, but enough to prevent adhesion.

Remedy 1:
Be sure the inkmaker knows the print sequence of the inks.

Remedy 2:
Prevent crystallization of the first-down ink. (See remedies for previous problem.)

Remedy 3:
Run the printed sheets through the drying oven of a spirit varnishing machine. Heating improves the adhesion.

Problem 15.   **Wet trapping.** Ink fails to trap in wet multicolor printing.

Cause A: Second-down ink is tackier than the first. This condition is particularly troublesome in metal decorating and in printing on nonabsorbent stocks like decal papers. With more absorbent stock, decreasing tack sequence is less important.

Remedy 1:
Use only tack-sequenced inks.

Remedy 2:
Reduce the tack of the ink that fails to trap properly. Obtain inks for multicolor presswork with tacks that are successively decreasing in order of the color sequence.

Remedy 3:
Increase the ink film thickness of an ink that will not trap. Thicker films are split more easily than thin ones.

Cause B: Improper color strength. This can result in having to run one color full and the following color spare, in which case the color run spare may not trap over the full color.

Remedy 1:
Use only tack-sequenced inks.

Remedy 2:
Do not run inks from different sets.

Remedy 3:
Use a set of multicolor wet process inks that is balanced for strength so that approximately equal amounts can be run.

Problem 16.   **Slur.**

Cause: Too much back-cylinder pressure in printing coated stocks;

too much plate-to-blanket pressure in printing from smooth, ungrained plates; unflat sheets rippling as they enter the impression nip; running too much ink on coated papers or running an ink that is too soft.

Remedy:
Run the ink and press according to standard back-cylinder pressure, plate and blanket packing, ink film thickness, and ink formulation. (See Chapter 2, Problem 4.)

Problem 17.   **Mottle or mottling.** Mottle is caused by an uneven penetration of ink into the paper. All machine-made papers are somewhat nonuniform. There is a greater amount of non-uniformity in heavier sheets; therefore, problems are more common with board than with book paper. Mottle is overcome by adjusting the ink so that either all or none of it penetrates the stock.

Cause A: Ink not properly adjusted to the stock.

Remedy 1:
Use an ink that will not show mottle on the sheet to be printed.

Remedy 2:
Increase the tack and length of the ink by adding body gum or water-resistant varnish.

Remedy 3:
Decrease the tack of the ink by adding a little heatset oil or no. 00 varnish.

Remedy 4:
Make a drying test of the ink on the paper to be printed before starting the job.

Cause B: Coatings with nonuniform ink absorbency. This condition can be shown by the K & N absorbency test.

Remedy:
Use a stiffer ink or add body gum or gloss varnish to make the ink less penetrating so it can dry with a uniform finish.

Cause C: Non-ink-receptive stock.

Comparison of long
and short inks

Remedy:
Use an ink with maximum color strength and tack.

Cause D: Uncoated stock with wild formation.

An ink drawdown
for evaluating such
characteristics as
color match and
comparative color
strength

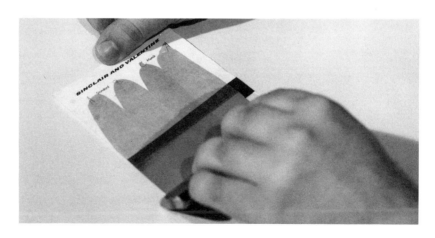

Remedy 1:
Replace the stock.

Remedy 2:
Use an ink with maximum color strength and minimum
penetration.

Cause E: Running too much ink on hard, non-ink-receptive papers.

Remedy:
Use an ink with greater color strength, and run less of it. Stiffening the ink may help.

Cause F: Excessive back-cylinder pressure.

Remedy:
Reduce the pressure.

Cause G: Too much dampening water. Moisture reduces the ink tack and also causes minute white spots in solids (snowflakiness).

Remedy:
Keep the amount of dampening to a minimum.

Problem 18. **Mottled appearance on plastic.**

Cause A: Dyne level too low or too high.

Remedy:
Use a plastic that is corona-treated with a surface energy from 40 to 50 dynes.

Cause B: Static buildup on the plastic.

Remedy 1:
Use static eliminators on the press.

Remedy 2:
Increase the relative humidity (RH) in the pressroom.

Cause C: Too much water emulsified into the ink.

Remedy:
Use inks with lower water pickup when printing on nonabsorbent substrates.

Cause D: Plasticizer or processing lubricants blooming to the surface resulting in a mottled appearance.

Remedy:
Replace the plastic.

Cause E: Nonuniform corona treatment.

Remedy:
Replace the plastic.

Problem 19. **Tinting.** Specks of ink can be seen on the printed sheets and may or may not be visible on the plate. The tint is not held tightly on the plate but can be washed off with a sponge or picked off with a moistened thumb. However, it quickly re-appears when printing resumes. (See Chapter 5, Problem 5.)

Cause A: Soaps or detergents in the dampening solution.

Remedy:
Never add soaps or detergents to the dampening solution. Rinse molleton covers thoroughly after washing. Use only dampening solution additives that have been recommended by reputable dealers.

Cause B: The dampening solution extracts wetting agents and/or chemicals from the paper coating, causing the ink to emulsify.

Remedy 1:
Change to another paper.

Remedy 2:
Try stiffening the ink with no. 8 or no. 10 long varnish or a water-resistant varnish.

Cause C: Inking rollers set so tightly that they emulsify ink and water.

Remedy:
Set inking rollers properly.

Cause D: Printing plate is slightly ink-sensitive because of residual plate coating on the nonimage areas.

Remedy:
The remedies for plate problems are treated in Chapter 5, "Press and Plate Problems."

Problem 20. **Piling or caking.** The ink piles or cakes on the rollers, plate, or blanket and fails to transfer properly.

Cause A: Ink is too short and lacks the fluidity necessary to make it transfer properly. Excess pigment content and excess emulsification cause the ink to become short.

Remedy 1:
Consult the inkmaker; purchase a longer ink.

Remedy 2:
Add a varnish that will make the ink longer. Ask the inkmaker which varnish to use.

Remedy 3:
Reduce the dampening to a minimum. (Some inks can become too short because they are waterlogged.) If this remedy does not help, have the ink made with a more water-resistant varnish.

Remedy 4:
Increase dampening. Increased water tends to wash away dust, dirt, and debris from the paper. This is the direct opposite of Remedy 2, but sometimes this remedy will work if the other does not.

Remedy 5:
Change papers. Dust or lint from the paper may work its way into the ink, making it short.

Remedy 6:
Avoid adding starch, talcum, or any other solid to the ink.

Cause B: Poorly ground ink containing too many coarse particles or aggregates. These are not transferred, but remain and build up a cake on the roller, plate, and blanket surfaces.

Remedy:
Return the ink to the inkmaker to have it reground.

Cause C: Ink contains a coarse, heavy pigment that piles or cakes.

Remedy:
Consult the inkmaker. Have the ink reformulated.

Cause D: Paper coating becomes tacky when moistened. In multicolor presswork, moisture applied by the first unit softens the coating so that some of it is picked up by the blanket on the second or later unit. This coating gradually builds up on the blanket in the middle halftone areas, forming "bumps" that cause slur and produce a mottled appearance.

Remedy 1:
Change to a paper that has better moisture resistance.

Remedy 2:
Apply a press size using a transparent white ink.

Remedy 3:
Printers report that sending the paper back to storage for a week often helps to solve the problem.

Problem 21.   **Ink backs away from the fountain roller.**

Cause: Ink remains in the fountain and fails to flow and replace the ink that is removed by the fountain roller. (See Chapter 2, Problem 2.)

Remedy 1:
Work the ink in the fountain frequently to keep it fluid, or install an ink fountain agitator.

Remedy 2:
With some inks, the addition of no. 3 or no. 4 long varnish will increase their length and flow properties.

Problem 22.   **Inks flies or mists.** Long ink films form long filaments when split on the press. These filaments break into fine droplets that spray around the press.

Cause A: Too much ink. Longer filaments form when a thick film is on the press rollers.

Remedy:
Substitute a more strongly colored ink, and run less of it.

Cause B: Ink is too long and too tacky.

Remedy 1:
Add shortening material such as a wax compound. Consult the inkmaker.

Remedy 2:
Increase dampening. (Curiously, water shortens the ink and reduces fly, one of the few benefits of running excess water.)

Cause C: Too little side-to-side motion of the oscillating rollers allows ink to form ridges on the rollers and increases ink misting.

Remedy:
Increase the oscillation until the ridging disappears.

Cause D: Too thick of an ink film on the fountain roller.

Formation of ink mist by the splitting of ink film emerging from roller nip

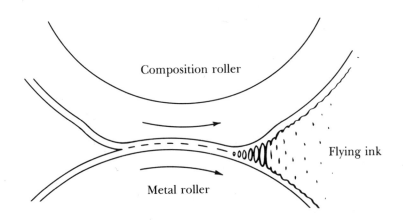

Remedy 1:
Tighten the fountain blade, and adjust the ratchet to increase the rotation of the roller.

Remedy 2:
Add a wax compound or other shortening material.

Problem 23.   **Color fades or burns out during drying.** This problem sometimes occurs with certain inorganic pigments in printing large solids or solid tints.

Cause: Not enough oxygen for complete drying.When the ink vehicle uses up the available oxygen, it takes the oxygen from certain inorganic pigments, burning out their colors. Heat generated during drying accelerates this reaction.

Remedy 1:
Wind the printed sheets two or three times during the first four hours after printing.

Remedy 2:
Use inks that do not burn out.

Index

Vacuum,
  sheet cleaner   87
  slow-down rollers   19
  timing   9
Varnish, use of   99, 104, 107–109, 111, 113, 114, 117–119,
Velcron   18

Wash marks   48, 49
Wavy-edged paper   16, 33, 78–80
Wet trapping   113
Wheel tension   16
White spots   52, 53, 85–88
Wrinkles, paper   12, 16, 77, 79, 80